APES AND PARROTS

APES AND PARROTS

AN ANTHOLOGY OF PARODIES
COLLECTED BY
J. C. SQUIRE

HERBERT JENKINS LIMITED
3 YORK STREET ST. JAMES'S
LONDON S.W.1 ❀   ❀   ❀

A
HERBERT
JENKINS'
BOOK

First printing . . *November 1928*
Second printing . . *February 1929*

Printed in Great Britain by Butler & Tanner Ltd., Frome and London

PREFACE

THERE have been anthologies of parodies before, and good ones ; but I hope that the appearance of this new one will be allowed to be justified since it includes a large number of modern parodies not previously brought into the company of their peers, and also since it is (to the best of my knowledge) the first to include prose parodies as well as verse. Even those venerable and excellent travesties of Johnson and Cobbett by the brothers Smith have been hitherto passed over.

The earlier parodies in the book will mostly be familiar to students of the art. They may even miss some familiar examples which they will expect to find. But imitations, however close, which did not amuse me, either incidentally, or by the force of their implied criticism, I have excluded. Most of Hawkins Browne's come into that category. Hogg's are near it ; but he has a delightful habit of occasionally breaking into superficially beautiful gibberish, which qualifies such a work as his utterly Coleridgean parody of Coleridge. Hogg, it may be added, is one of several genuine poets who have enriched our literature with classic parodies— Coleridge and Swinburne (perhaps the greatest of all) being others. But since sensitiveness to fine shades of meaning and sound is among the essential qualities of a parodist, this is not surprising.

5

The prose parodies are fewer than the others. They increase as time passes, like the verse parodies : the art as a whole came into being with the practice of literary criticism as we know it, and has grown with it.   Prose parodies are scarcer than parodies in verse, for one evident reason : the scale of them, if they are to be thoroughly effective, must be ampler.   Even the best of them, being mostly parodies of novelists, cannot exhibit or caricature the larger characteristics of the authors : the " architecture " of their stories, their devices for developing character, their kind of panoramas. It is one thing for a man of quick apprehension to " throw off " a brief lyric that might be by Swinburne : it is another to sit down and summarize all the qualities of Dickens' narratives in ten pages of careful prose.   Stone parodies (deliberate I mean) of sculpture are, by the same token, rarer still.   A man will not spend six months on a skit.

The prose pages would have been slightly more numerous had I drawn upon the Nonsense Novels of Thackeray and Bret Harte.   Thackeray's appear to me too tame, Harte's too flimsy : both have suffered by the passage of time.   The parodist who is topical runs risks, like other topical commentators : if his subject loses interest so must his parody, however brilliant.   If an author be no longer read a parody of him will be no longer readable : unless indeed the parodist has largely relied for his effect upon jokes not strictly relevant to his business.   Authors pass ; so do themes, Lewis Carroll's " Hiawatha " parody about cameras no longer raises a smile, as cameras are now common-

places. Sir Owen Seaman's superb parody of
Maurice Hewlett has now lost half its force, perfect
as it is in its grasp of Hewlett's mode of thinking
and writing : it was an allegory, full of topical
details, of the Boer War, and few people now
remember the details of the Boer War. Even his
Alfred Austin, which I could not resist, is less
effective than it was, since the present generation
is so imperfectly familiar with Austin's banality
and the comic history of his appointment. Notes,
in many instances, might have helped : but how
can one load an anthology of quips with the appara-
tus of a German edition of Juvenal ?

I ask the indulgence of readers for having, for
once, succumbed to the unpleasant habit of including
some of the anthologist's own works : basely
falling back, for excuse, upon the solicitation of
friends. And I thank the following for permission
to reprint copyright " material " :

TITLE	AUTHOR	PUBLISHER
TOP-SIDE GALOW	C. G. Leland	Kegan, Paul, Trench. Trubner & Co.,Ltd
THE COCK AND THE BULL	C. S. Calverley	G. Bell & Sons, Ltd.
BEER	,,	,,
THE AULD WIFE	,,	,,
LOVERS AND A REFLECTION	,,	,,
PROVERBIAL PHILOSOPHY	,,	,,
FATHER WILLIAM	Lewis Carroll	Macmillan & Co.,Ltd
THE VOICE OF THE LOBSTER	,,	,,
TURTLE SOUP	,,	,,
THE BOLD MOUNSEER	W. S. Gilbert	,,
NEPHELIDIA	A. C. Swinburne	William Heinemann Ltd.
THE HIGHER PANTEHISM IN A NUTSHELL	,,	,,
THE POET AND THE WOOD-LOUSE	,,	,,
THE PERSON OF THE HOUSE : THE KID	,,	,,
'TWAS EVER THUS	Henry S. Leigh	Chatto & Windus.

TITLE	AUTHOR	PUBLISHER
THE CIGARETTE GATHERER	E. V. Knox	Methuen & Co., Ltd
MYSTERY	,,	,,
THE PECULIAR BIRD	,,	,,
THE WAY HOME	S. Baghot de a Bere	—
VARIATIONS ON AN AIR	G. K. Chesterton	Cecil Palmer
HE SPORTS BY HIMSELF	Susan Miles	—
THE NEW VICAR OF BRAY	Colin D. B. Ellis	Basil Blackwell.

APES AND PARROTS

Samuel Wesley (1666–1735)

A PINDARIC ON THE GRUNTING OF A HOG

FREEBORN Pindaric never does refuse
   Either a lofty or a humble muse :—
Now in proud Sophoclean buskins sings
   Of heroes and of kings,
  Mighty numbers, mighty things ;
   Now out of sight she flies,
   Rowing with gaudy wings
   Across the stormy skies ;
    Then down again
    Herself she flings,
Without uneasiness or pain,
    To lice and dogs,
    To cows and hogs,
And follows their melodious grunting o'er the plain.

  Harmonious hog, draw near !
   No bloody butcher's here,—
   Thou needst not fear.
Harmonious hog, draw near, and from thy beauteous
     snout
  (Whilst we attend with ear,
  Like thine, pricked up devout,
To taste thy sugary voice, which here and there.

With wanton curls, vibrates around the circling
        air),
  Harmonious hog ! warble some anthem out !
As sweet as those which quavering Monks, in days
        of yore,
      With us did roar,
      When they (alas
That the hard-hearted abbot such a coil should keep,
    And cheat 'em of their first, their sweetest sleep !)
    When they were ferreted up to midnight mass :
  Why should not the pigs on organs play,
        As well as they ?
    Dear hog ! thou king of meat !
    So near thy lord, mankind,
  The nicest taste can scarce a difference find !
  No more may I thy glorious gammons eat—
      No more
  Partake of the free farmer's Christmas store,
Black puddings which with fat would make your
        mouth run o'er—
If I (though I should ne'er so long the sentence
        stay,
And in my large ears' scale the thing ne'er so
        discreetly weigh),
  If I can find a difference in the notes
    Belched from the applauded throats
  Of rotten playhouse songsters all divine,—
If any difference I can find between their notes and
        thine,
      A noise they keep, with tune and out of tune,
      And round and flat,
        High, low, and this and that,
      That Algebra or thou or I might understand
        as soon.

Like the confounding lute's innumerable strings
    One of them sings.
Thy easier music's ten times more divine :
More like the one-stringed, deep, majestic trump-
      marine.
Prithee strike up, and cheer this drooping heart of
      mine.
  Not the sweet harp that's claimed by Jews,
Nor that which to the far more ancient Welsh
      belongs,
  Nor that which the wild Irish use,
Frighting even their own wolves with loud hub-
      bubbaboos,
  Nor Indian dance with Indian songs,
    Nor yet
    (Which how should I so long forget ?)
  The crown of all the rest,
  The very cream o' the jest,
  Amphion's noble lyre—the tongs ;
  Nor, though poetic Jordan bite his thumbs
At the bold world, my Lord Mayor's flutes and
      kettledrums ;
  Not all this instrumental dare
With thy soft, ravishing, vocal music ever to
      compare !

John Philips (1676–1709)

THE SPLENDID SHILLING
(*Milton*)

HAPPY the Man, who void of Cares and Strife,
    In silken, or in Leathern Purse retains
A *Splendid Shilling* : he nor hears with Pain

New Oysters cry'd, nor sighs for cheerful Ale ;
But with his friends, when Nightly Mists arise,
To *Juniper's-Magpye*, or *Town-Hall* repairs :
Where, mindful of the Nymph, whose wanton
  eye
Transfixed his Soul, and kindled Amorous Flames,
CHLOE, or PHILLIS ; he each Circling Glass
Wisheth her Health, and Joy, and equal Love.
Mean while, he smoaks, and laughs at Merry
  Tale,
Or *Pun* ambiguous, or *Conundrum* quaint.
But I, whom griping Penury surrounds,
And hunger, sure Attendant upon Want,
With scanty Offals, and small acid Tiff
(Wretched Repast !) my meagre Corps sustain :
Then solitary walk, or doze at home
In garret vile, and with a warming Puff
Regale chill'd Fingers ; or from Tube as black
As Winter-Chimney, or well-polish'd Jet,
Exhale *Mundungus*, ill-perfuming Scent :
Not blacker Tube, nor of a shorter Size
Smoaks *Cambro-Britain* (vers'd in Pedigree,
Sprung from *Cadwalader* and *Arthur*, Kings
Full famous in Romantick Tale) when he
O'er many a craggy Hill and barren Cliff,
Upon a Cargo of fam'd *Cestrian* Cheese,
High over-shadowing Rides, with a design
To vend his Wares, or at th' *Arvonian* Mart,
Or *Maridunum*, or the Ancient Town
Yclip'd *Brechinia*, or where *Vaga's* Stream
Encircles *Ariconium*, fruitful Soil !
Whence flow Nectareous Wines, that well may
  vie
With *Massic*, *Setin*, or renown'd *Falern*.

Thus, while my joyless Minutes tedious flow,
With looks demure, and silent Pace, a *Dun*
Horrible Monster! hated by Gods and Men,
To my Aerial Citadel ascends,
With Vocal Heel thrice thund'ring at my Gate,
With hideous Accent Thrice he calls; I know
The Voice ill-boding, and the solemn Sound.
What should I do! or whither turn? Amaz'd,
Confounded, to the dark Recess I fly
Of Woodhole; strait my bristling Hairs erect
Thro' sudden Fear; a chilly Sweat bedews
My shud'ring Limbs, and (wonderful to tell!)
My Tongue forgets her Faculty of Speech;
So horrible he seems! his faded Brow
Entrench'd with many a Frown, and Comic Beard,
And spreading Band, admir'd by Modern Saints,
Disastrous Acts forebode; in his Right Hand
Long Scrolls of Paper solemnly he waves,
With Characters, and Figures dire inscrib'd,
Grievous to Mortal Eyes; (ye Gods avert
Such Plagues from Righteous Men!) Behind him
 stalks
Another Monster, not unlike himself,
Sullen of aspect, by the Vulgar call'd
A *Catchpole*, whose polluted Hands the Gods
With Force incredible, and Magick Charms
Erst have endu'd, if he his ample Palm
Should haply on ill-fated Shoulder lay
Of Debtor, strait his Body to the Touch
Obsequious, (as whilom Knights were wont)
To some Inchanted Castle is convey'd
Where Gates impregnable, and coercive Chains
In Durance strict detain him, till in form
Of Money, PALLAS sets the Captive free.

Beware, ye Debtors, when ye walk beware,
Be circumspect ; oft with insidious Ken
This Caitif eyes your Steps aloof, and oft
Lies perdue in a Nook, or gloomy Cave,
Prompt to inchant some inadvertent Wretch
With his unhallow'd Touch. So (Poets sing)
Grimalkin to Domestick Vermin sworn
An everlasting Foe, with watchful Eye
Lies Nightly brooding o'er a chinky Gap
Protending her fell Claws, to thoughtless Mice
Sure Ruin. So her disembowell'd Web
Arachne in a Hall, or Kitchin spreads,
Obvious to vagrant Flies : she secret stands
Within her woven Cell ; the Humming Prey,
Regardless of their Fate, rush on the Toils
Inextricable, nor will aught avail
Their Arts, or Arms, or Shapes of lovely Hue :
The Wasp insidious, and the buzzing Drone,
And Butterfly proud of expanded Wings
Distinct with Gold, entangled in her Snares,
Useless Resistance make : With eager Strides,
She tow'ring flies to her expected Spoils ;
Then, with envenomed Jaws the vital Blood
Drinks of reluctant Foes, and to her Cave
Their bulky Carcasses triumphant drags.

So pass my Days. But when Nocturnal Shades
This World invelop, and th' inclement Air
Persuades Men to repel benumming Frosts
With pleasant Wines, and crackling Blaze of Wood ;
Me lonely sitting, nor the glimmering Light
Of Make-weight Candle, nor the joyous Talk
Of loving Friend delights ; distress'd, forlorn,
Amidst the Horrors of the tedious Night,

Darkling I sigh, and feed with dismal Thoughts
My anxious Mind ; or sometimes mournful Verse
Indite, and sing of Groves and Myrtle Shades,
Or desperate Lady near a purling Stream
Or Lover pendant on a Willow-Tree.
Mean while, I labour with eternal Drought,
And restless writh, and rave ; my parched Throat
Finds no Relief, nor heavy Eyes Repose :
But if a Slumber haply does invade
My weary Limbs, my Fancy's still awake,
Thoughtful of Drink, and eager, in a Dream,
Tipples imaginary Pots of Ale,
In vain ; awake I find the settled thirst
Still gnawing, and the pleasant Phantom curse.

Thus do I Live from Pleasure quite debarr'd,
Nor taste the Fruits that the Sun's genial Rays
Mature, *John-Apple*, nor the downy *Peach*,
Nor *Walnut* in rough-furrow'd Coat secure,
Nor *Medlar*-Fruit, delicious in decay :
Afflictions great ! yet Greater still remain :
My *Galligaskins* that have long withstood
The Winter's Fury, and incroaching Frosts,
By Time subdu'd, (what will not Time subdue !)
An horrid Chasm disclose, with Orifice
Wide, discontinuous ; at which the Winds
Eurus and *Auster*, and the dreadful Force
Of *Boreas*, that congeals the *Cronian* Waves,
Tumultuous enter with dire chilling Blasts,
Portending Agues. Thus a well-fraught Ship
Long sail'd secure, or thro' th' Ægean Deep,
Or the *Ionian*, till Cruising near
The *Lilybean* Shore, with hideous Crush
On *Scylla*, or *Charybdis* (dang'rous Rocks)

She strikes rebounding, whence the shatter'd Oak,
So fierce a Shock unable to withstand,
Admits the Sea ; in at the gaping Side
The crowding Waves gush with impetuous Rage,
Resistless, Overwhelming ; Horrors seize
The Mariners, Death in their Eyes appears.
They Stare, they Lave, they Pump, they Swear,
    they Pray :
(Vain efforts !) still the battering Waves rush in,
Implacable, till delug'd by the Foam,
The Ship sinks found'ring in the vast Abyss.

Alexander Pope (1688–1744)

THE HAPPY LIFE OF A COUNTRY PARSON

(*Swift*)

PARSON, these things in thy possessing
    Are better than the bishop's blessing :
A wife that makes conserves ; a steed
That carries double when there's need ;
October store, and best Virginia,
Tithe-pig, and mortuary guinea ;
Gazettes sent gratis down, and frank'd ;
For which thy patron's meekly thank'd ;
A large Concordance, bound long since ;
Sermons to Charles the First, when Prince ;
A chronicle of ancient standing ;
A Chrysostom to smooth thy band in ;
The Polyglott—three parts—my text :
Howbeit,—likewise—now to my next :

Lo here the Septuagint,—and Paul,
To sum the whole,—and close of all.
He that has these, may pass his life,
Drink with the Squire, and kiss his wife ;
On Sundays preach, and eat his fill ;
And fast on Fridays—if he will ;
Toast Church and Queen, explain the news,
Talk with churchwardens about pews,
Pray heartily for some new gift,
And shake his head at Doctor Swift.

Henry Carey (1693(?)–1743)

NAMBY PAMBY

(*A. Phillips*)

ALL ye poets of the age,
    All ye witlings of the stage,
Learn your jingles to reform :
Cross your numbers and conform,
Let the little verses flow
Gently, sweetly, row by row.
Let the verse the subject fit,
Little subject, little wit.
Namby Pamby is your guide,
Albion's joy, Hibernia's pride.

.   .   .

He no longer writes of mammy
Andromache and her lammy
Hanging panging at the breast
Of a matron most distrest.
Now the venal poet sings
Baby clouts and baby things,

Baby dolls and baby houses,
Little misses, little spouses ;
Little playthings, little toys,
Little girls and little boys.
As an actor does his part
So the nurses get by heart
Namby Pamby's little rhymes,
Little jingles, little chimes.
Namby Pamby ne'er will die
While the nurse sings lullaby.
Namby Pamby's doubly mild,
Once a man and twice a child ;
To his hanging sleeves restored
Now he foots it like a lord ;
Now he pumps his little wits,
All by little tiny bits.
Now, methinks, I hear him say
Boys and girls come out to play,
Moon does shine as bright as day.
Now my Namby Pamby's found
Sitting on the Friar's ground,
Picking silver, picking gold,
Namby Pamby's never old.
Bally-cally they begin,
Namby Pamby still keeps in.
Namby Pamby is no clown,
London Bridge is broken down :
Now he courts the gay Ladee
Dancing o'er the Lady-lee :
Now he sings of lick-spit liar
Burning in the brimstone fire ;
Liar, liar, lick-spit, lick,
Turn about the candle-stick.
Now he sings of Jacky Horner

Sitting in the chimney corner
Eating of a Christmas pie,
Putting in his thumb, oh, fie !
Putting in, oh, fie ! his thumb !
Pulling out, oh, strange ! a plum.

.   .   .   .

Guard him, ye poetic powers,
Watch his minutes, watch his hours :
Let your tuneful Nine inspire him,
Let poetic fury fire him :
Let the poets one and all
To his genius victims fall.

Isaac Hawkins Browne (1705–1760)

A PIPE OF TOBACCO
Imitation V.
(*Pope*)

BLEST Leaf ! whose aromatic Gales dispense
To Templars Modesty, to Parsons sense :
So raptur'd Priests, at fam'd Dodona's Shrine
Drank Inspiration from the stream divine.
Poison that cures, a Vapour that affords
Content, more solid than the Smile of Lords :
Rest to the Weary, to the Hungry food,
The Last Kind refuge of the Wise and Good :
Inspir'd by Thee, dull Cits adjust the Scale
Of Europe's peace, when other Statesmen fail.
By Thee protected, and thy Sister, Beer,
Poets rejoice nor think the Bailiff near.
Nor less, the Critic owns thy genial Aid,
While supperless he plies the piddling trade.
What tho' to Love and soft Delights a Foe,

By Ladies hated, hated by the Beau,
Yet social Freedom, long to Courts unknown,
Fair Health, fair Truth and Virtue are thy own.
Come to thy Poet, come with healing Wings
And let me taste Thee, unexcis'd by Kings.

Dr. Samuel Johnson (1709–1784)

THE TURNIP-CRIER
(The Epigram)

IF a man who turnips cries
    Cry not when his father dies,
Is it not a proof he'd rather
Have a turnip than his father ?

HATS AND THE MAN
(The Ballad)

I PUT my hat upon my head
    And walked into the Strand,
And there I met another man
With his hat in his hand.

Catherine Maria Fanshawe (1765–1834)

FRAGMENTS IN IMITATION OF
WORDSWORTH
(W. Wordsworth)

THERE is a river clear and fair,
    'Tis neither broad nor narrow ;
It winds a little here and there—

It winds about like any hare ;
And then it holds as straight a course
As, on the turnpike road, a horse,
Or, through the air, an arrow.

The trees that grow upon the shore
Have grown a hundred years or more ;
So long there is no knowing :
Old Daniel Dobson does not know
When first those trees began to grow ;
But still they grew, and grew, and grew,
As if they'd nothing else to do,
But ever must be growing.

The impulses of air and sky
Have reared their stately heads so high,
And clothed their boughs with green ;
Their leaves the dews of evening quaff,—
And when the wind blows loud and keen,
I've seen the jolly timbers laugh,
And shake their sides with merry glee—
Wagging their heads in mockery.

Fixed are their feet in solid earth
Where winds can never blow ;
But visitings of deeper birth
Have reached their roots below.
For they have gained the river's brink,
And of the living waters drink.

There's little Will, a five years' child—
He is my youngest boy ;
To look on eyes so fair and wild,
It is a very joy.

He hath conversed with sun and shower,
And dwelt with every idle flower,
As fresh and gay as them.
He loiters with the briar-rose,—
The blue-bells are his play-fellows,
That dance upon their slender stem.

And I have said, my little Will,
Why should he not continue still
A thing of Nature's rearing ?
A thing beyond the world's control—
A living vegetable soul—
No human sorrow fearing.

It were a blessed sight to see
That child become a willow-tree,
His brother trees among.
He'd be four times as tall as me,
And live three times as long.

John Hookham Frere (1769–1846)

ISABELLE

(*S. T. Coleridge*)

CAN there be a moon in heaven to-night,
That the hill and the grey cloud seem so light ?
The air is whitened by some spell,
For there is no moon, I know it well :
On this third day, the sages say,
('Tis wonderful how well they know),
The moon is journeying far away,
Bright somewhere in a heaven below.

It is a strange and lovely night,
A greyish pale, but not white!
Is it rain, or is it dew,
That falls so thick I see its hue?
In rays it follows, one, two, three,
Down the air so merrily,
Said Isabelle, so let it be!

Why does the Lady Isabelle
Sit in the damp and dewy dell
Counting the racks of drizzly rain,
And how often the Rail cries over again?
For she's harping, harping in the brake,
Craik, craik—craik, craik.—
Ten times nine, and thrice eleven;—
That last call was an hundred and seven.
Craik, craik—the hour is near—
Let it come, I have no fear!
Yet it is a dreadful work, I wis,
Such doings in a night like this!

Sounds the river harsh and loud?
The stream sounds harsh, but not loud.
There is a cloud that seems to hover,
By western hill the churchyard over,
What is it like?—'Tis like a whale;
'Tis like a shark with half the tail,
Not half, but third and more;
Now 'tis a wolf, and now a boar;
Its face is raised—it cometh here;
Let it come—there is no fear.
There's two for heaven, and ten for hell,
Let it come—'tis well—'tis well
Said the Lady Isabelle.

What ails that little cut-tailed whelp,
That it continues to yelp, yelp ?
Yelp, yelp, and it turns its eye
Up to the tree and half to the sky,
Half to the sky and full to the cloud,
And still it whines and barks aloud.
Why I should dread I cannot tell ;
There is a spirit ; I know it well !
I see it in yon falling beam—
Is it a vision or a dream ?
It is no dream, full well I know,
I have a woful deed to do !
Hush, hush, thou little murmurer ;
I tell thee hush—the dead are near !

If thou knewest all, poor tailless whelp,
Well mightest thou tremble, growl, and yelp ;
But thou knowest nothing, hast no part,
(Simple and stupid as thou art)
Save gratitude and truth of heart.
But they are coming by this way
That have been dead for a year and a day ;
Without challenge, without change,
They shall have their full revenge !
They have been sent to wander in woe
In the lands of flame, and the lands of snow ;
But those that are dead
Shall the greensward tread,
And those that are living
Shall soon be dead !
None to pity them, none to help !
Thou mayest quake, my cut-tailed whelp !

There are two from the grave
That I fain would save ;
Full hard is the weird
For the young and the brave !
Perchance they are rapt in vision sweet,
While the passing breezes kiss their feet ;
And they are dreaming of joy and love !
Well, let them go—there's room above.

There are three times three, and three to these
Count as you will, by twos or threes !
Three for the gallows, and three for the wave,
Three to roast behind the stone,
And three that shall never see the grave
Until the day and the hour are gone !
For retribution is mine alone !
The cloud is redder in its hue,
The hour is near, and vengeance due ;
It cannot, and it will not fail,—
'Tis but a step to Borrowdale !
Why shouldest thou love and follow me ?
Poor faithful thing ! I pity thee !

Up rose the Lady Isabelle,
I may not of her motion tell,
Yet thou mayest look upon her frame ;
Look on it with a passing eye,
But think not thou upon the same,
Turn away and ask not why ;
But if thou darest look again,
Mad of heart and seared of brain,
Thou shalt never look again !

What can ail that short-tailed whelp ?
'Tis either behind or far before,
And it hath changed its whining yelp
To a shortened yuff—its little core
Seems bursting with terror and dismay,
Yuff, yuff—hear how it speeds away.
Hold thy peace, thou yemering thing,
The very night-wind's slumbering,
And thou wilt wake to woe and pain
Those that must never wake again.

Meet is its terror and its flight,
There's one on the left and two on the right !
But save the paleness of the face,
All is beauty and all is grace !
The earth and air are tinged with blue ;
There are no footsteps in the dew ;
Is this to wandering spirits given,
Such stillness on the face of heaven ?
The fleecy clouds that sleep above
Are like the wing of beauteous dove,
And the leaf of the elm tree does not move !
Yet they are coming ! and they are three !
Jesu ! Maria ! can it be !

THE CONCLUSION

Sleep on, fair maiden of Borrowdale !
Sleep !   O sleep ! and do not wake !
Dream of the dance, till the foot so pale,
And the beauteous ankle shiver and shake ;
Till thou shalt press, with feeling bland,
Thine own fair breast with lover's hand.

Thy heart is light as summer breeze,
Thy heart is joyous as the day ;
Man never form of angel sees,
But thou art fair as they !
So lovers weep, and so they say,
So thine shall weep for many a day !
The hour's at hand, O woe is me !
For they are coming, and they are three !

A FABLE

(Dryden)

A DINGY donkey, formal and unchanged,
    Browsed in the lane and o'er the common
    ranged,
Proud of his ancient asinine possessions,
Free from the panniers of the grave professions,
He lived at ease ; and chancing once to find
A lion's skin, the fancy took his mind
To personate the monarch of the wood ;
And for a time the stratagem held good.
He moved with so majestical a pace
That bears and wolves and all the savage race
Gazed in admiring awe, ranging aloof
Not over-anxious for a clearer proof—
Longer he might have triumph'd—but alas !
In an unguarded hour it came to pass
He bray'd aloud ; and show'd himself an ass !

The moral of this tale I could not guess
Till Mr. Landor sent his works to press.

George Canning (1770–1827)

THE FRIEND OF HUMANITY AND THE KNIFE-GRINDER
(*Robert Southey*)

FRIEND OF HUMANITY

NEEDY knife-grinder ! whither are you going ?
   Rough is the road, your wheel is out of order—
Bleak blows the blast ;—your hat has got a hole
    in't,
      So have your breeches !

' Weary knife-grinder ! little think the proud ones
Who in their coaches roll along the turnpike-
Road, what hard work 'tis crying all day, ' Knives
    and
      Scissors to grind O ! '

' Tell me, knife-grinder, how came you to grind
    knives ?
Did some rich man tyrannically use you ?
Was it the squire ? or parson of the parish ?
      Or the attorney ?

Was it the squire, for killing of his game ? or
Covetous parson, for his tithes distraining ?
Or roguish lawyer, made you lose your little
      All in a lawsuit ?

(Have you not read the Rights of Man, by Tom
    Paine ?),
Drops of compassion tremble on my eyelids,
Ready to fall as soon as you have told your
      Pitiful story."

Knife-Grinder

" Story ! God bless you ! I have none to tell, sir,
　　Only last night a-drinking at the Chequers
This poor old hat and breeches, as you see, were
　　　　Torn in a scuffle.

" Constables came up for to take me into
　　Custody ; they took me before the justice ;
Justice Oldmixon put me in the parish
　　　　Stocks for a vagrant.

" I should be glad to drink your Honour's health in
　　A pot of beer, if you will give me sixpence ;
But for my part, I never love to meddle
　　　　With politics, sir."

Friend of Humanity

" I give thee sixpence ! I will see thee damn'd
　　　　first—
Wretch ! whom no sense of wrongs can rouse to
　　　　vengeance—
Sordid, unfeeling, reprobate, degraded,
　　　　Spiritless outcast ! "

[*Kicks the Knife-grinder, overturns his wheel, and
　　exit in a transport of republican enthusiasm and
　　universal philanthropy.*]

INSCRIPTION
(*Robert Southey*)

FOR one long term, or e'er her trial came,
　　Here Brownrigg linger'd. Often have these cells
Echoed her blasphemies, as with shrill voice
She scream'd for fresh Geneva. Not to her

Did the blithe fields of Tothill, or thy street,
St. Giles, its fair varieties expand ;
Till at the last, in slow-drawn cart, she went
To execution. Dost thou ask her crime ?
SHE WHIPP'D TWO FEMALE PRENTICES TO DEATH,
AND HID THEM IN THE COAL-HOLE. For her mind
Shaped strictest plans of discipline. Sage schemes !
Such as Lycurgus taught, when at the shrine
Of the Orthyan Goddess he bade flog
The little Spartans : such as erst chastised
Our Milton, when at college. For this act
Did Brownrigg swing. Harsh laws ! But time
    shall come,
When France shall reign, and laws be all repeal'd !

James Hogg (1770–1835)

THE FLYING TAILOR
(*Wordsworth*)

IF ever chance or choice thy footsteps lead
   Into that green and flowery burial-ground
That compasseth with sweet and mournful smiles
The Church of Grasmere,—by the eastern gate
Enter—and underneath a stunted yew,
Some three yards distant from the gravel-walk,
On the left-hand side, thou wilt espy a grave,
With unelaborate headstone beautified,
Conspicuous 'mid the other stoneless heaps
'Neath which the children of the valley lie.
There pause—and with no common feelings read
This short inscription—" Here lies buried
The Flying Tailor, aged twenty-nine ! "

Him from his birth unto his death I knew,
And many years before he had attained
The fulness of his fame, I prophesied
The triumphs of that youth's agility,
And crowned him with that name which afterwards
He nobly justified—and dying left
To fame's eternal blazon—read it here—
" The Flying Tailor ! "

It is somewhat strange
That his mother was a cripple, and his father
Long way declined into the vale of years,
When their son Hugh was born. At first the babe
Was sickly, and a smile was seen to pass
Across the midwife's cheek, when, holding up
The sickly wretch, she to the father said,
"A fine man-child ! " What else could they expect !
The mother being, as I said before,
A cripple, and the father of the child
Long way declined into the vale of years.
But mark the wondrous change—ere he was put
By his mother into breeches, Nature strung
The muscular part of his economy
To an unusual strength, and he could leap,
All unimpeded by his petticoats,
Over the stool on which his mother sat
When carding wool, or cleansing vegetables,
Or meek performing other household tasks.
Cunning he watched his opportunity,
And oft, as house affairs did call her thence,
Overleapt Hugh, a perfect whirligig,
More than six inches o'er the astonished stool !
What boots it to narrate, how at leap-frog
Over the breeched and unbreeched villagers

He shone conspicuous ?   Leap-frog do I say ?
Vainly so named.   What though in attitude
The Flying Taylor aped the croaking race
When issuing from the weed-entangled pool,
Tadpoles no more, they seek the new-mown fields,
A jocund people, bouncing to and fro
Amid the odorous clover—while amazed
The grasshopper sits idle on the stalk
With folded pinions and forgets to sing.
Frog-like, no doubt, in attitude he was ;
But sure his bounds across the village green
Seemed to my soul—(my soul for ever bright
With purest beams of sacred poesy)—
Like bounds of red deer on the Highland hill,
When, close environed by the tinchel's chain,
He lifts his branchy forehead to the sky,
Then o'er the many-headed multitude
Springs belling half in terror, half in rage,
And fleeter than the sunbeam or the wind
Speeds to his cloud-lair on the mountain-top.

   No more of this—suffice it to narrate,
In his tenth year he was apprenticed
Unto a Master Tailor, by a strong
And regular indenture of seven years,
Commencing from the date the parchment bore.
And ending on a certain day, that made
The term complete of seven solar years.
Oft have I heard him say, that at this time
Of life he was most wretched ; for, constrained
To sit all day cross-legged upon a board,
The natural circulation of the blood
Thereby was oft impeded, and he felt
So numbed at times, that when he strove to rise

Up from his work, he could not, but fell back
Among the shreds and patches that bestrewed
With various colours, brightening gorgeously,
The board all round him—patch of warlike red
With which he patched the regimental suits
Of a recruiting military troop,
At that time stationed in a market-town
At no great distance—eke of solemn black
Shreds of no little magnitude, with which
The parson's Sunday coat was then repairing,
That in the new-roofed church he might appear
With fitting dignity—and gravely fill
The sacred seat of pulpit eloquence,
Cheering with doctrinal point and words of faith
The poor man's heart, and from the shallow wit
Of atheist drying up each argument,
Or sharpening his own weapons, only to turn
Their point against himself, and overthrow
His idols with the very enginery
Reared 'gainst the structure of our English Church.

Oft too, when striving all he could to finish
The stated daily task, the needle's point,
Slanting insidious from the eluded stitch,
Hath pinched his finger, by the thimble's mail
In vain defended, and the crimson blood
Distained the lining of some wedding-suit ;
A dismal omen ! that to mind like his,
Apt to perceive in slightest circumstance
Mysterious meaning, yielded sore distress
And feverish perturbation, so that oft
He scarce could eat his dinner—nay, one night
He swore to run from his apprenticeship,
And go on board a first-rate man-of-war,

From Plymouth lately come to Liverpool,
Where, in the stir and tumult of a crew
Composed of many nations, 'mid the roar
Of wave and tempest, and the deadlier voice
Of battle, he might strive to mitigate
The fever that consumed his mighty heart.

But other doom was his. That very night
A troop of tumblers came into the village,
Tumbler, equestrian, mountebank,—on wire,
On rope, on horse, with cup and balls, intent
To please the gaping multitude, and win
The coin from labour's pocket—small perhaps
Each separate piece of money, but when joined
Making a good round sum, destined ere long
All to be melted (so these lawless folk
Name spending coin in loose debauchery),
Melted into ale—or haply stouter cheer,
Gin diuretic, or the liquid flame
Of baneful brandy, by the smuggler brought
From the French coast in shallop many-oared,
Skulking by night round headland and through
        bay,
Afraid of the king's cutter, or the barge
Of cruising frigate, armed with chosen men,
And with her sweeps across the foamy waves
Moving most beautiful with measured strokes.

It chanced that as he threw a somerset
Over three horses (each of larger size
Than our small mountain-breed), one of the troop
Put out his shoulder, and was otherwise
Considerably bruised, especially
About the loins and back. So he became

Useless unto that wandering company,
And likely to be felt a sore expense
To men just on the eve of bankruptcy ;
So the master of the troop determined
To leave him in the workhouse, and proclaimed
That if there was a man among the crowd
Willing to fill his place and able too,
Now was the time to show himself.   Hugh Thwaites
Heard the proposal, as he stood apart
Striving with his own soul—and with a bound
He leapt into the circle, and agreed
To supply the place of him who had been hurt.
A shout of admiration and surprise
Then tore heaven's concave, and completely filled
The little field, where near a hundred people
Were standing in a circle round and fair.
Oft have I striven by meditative power,
And reason working 'mid the various forms
Of various occupations and professions,
To explain the cause of one phenomenon,
That, since the birth of science, hath remained
A bare enunciation, unexplained
By any theory, or mental light
Streamed on it by the imaginative will,
Or spirit musing in the cloudy shrine,
The penetralia of the immortal soul.
I now allude to that most curious fact,
That 'mid a given number, say threescore,
Of tailors, more men of agility
Will issue out, than from an equal show
From any other occupation—say
Smiths, barbers, bakers, butchers, or the like.
Let me not seem presumptuous, if I strive
This subject to illustrate ; nor, while I give

My meditations to the world, will I
Conceal from it, that much I have to say
I learnt from one who knows the subject well
In theory and practice—need I name him?
The light-heeled author of the Isle of Palms,
Illustrious more for leaping than for song.

    First, then, I would lay down this principle,
That all excessive action by the law
Of nature tends unto repose. This granted,
All action not excessive must partake
The nature of excessive action—so
That in all human beings who keep moving,
Unconscious cultivation of repose
Is going on in silence. Be it so.
Apply to men of sedentary lives
This leading principle, and we behold
That, active in their inactivity,
And unreposing in their long repose,
They are, in fact, the sole depositaries
Of all the energies by others wasted,
And come at last to teem with impulses
Of muscular motion, not to be withstood,
And either giving vent unto themselves
In numerous feats of wild agility,
Or terminating in despair and death.

    Now, of all sedentary lives, none seems
So much so as the tailor's.—Weavers use
Both arms and legs, and, we may safely add,
Their bodies too, for arms and legs can't move
Without the body—as the waving branch
Of the green oak disturbs his glossy trunk.
Not so the tailor—for he sits cross-legged,

Cross-legged for ever! save at times of meals,
In bed, or when he takes his little walk
From shop to alehouse, picking, as he goes,
Stray patch of fustian, cloth, or cassimere,
Which, as by natural instinct, he discerns,
Though soiled with mud, and by the passing wheel
Bruised to attenuation 'gainst the stones.

Here then we pause—and need no farther go;
We have reached the sea-mark of our utmost sail.
Now let me trace the effect upon his mind
Of this despised profession. Deem not thou,
O rashly deem not, that his boyish days
Past at the shop-board, when the stripling bore
With bashful feeling of apprenticeship
The name of Tailor; deem not that his soul
Derived no genial influence from a life,
Which, although haply adverse in the main
To the growth of intellect, and the excursive power,
Yet in its ordinary forms possessed
A constant influence o'er his passing thoughts,
Moulded his appetences, and his will,
And wrought out, by the work of sympathy
Between his bodily and mental form,
Rare correspondence, wondrous unity!
Perfect—complete—and fading not away.
While on his board cross-legged he used to sit,
Shaping of various garments to his mind,
An image rose of every character
For whom each special article was framed,
Coat, waistcoat, breeches. So at last his soul
Was like a storehouse, filled with images,
By musing hours of solitude supplied.
Nor did his ready fingers shape the cut

Of villager's uncouth habiliments
With greater readiness, than did his mind
Frame corresponding images of those
Whose corporal measurement the neat-marked
    paper
In many a mystic notch for aye retained.
Hence, more than any man I ever knew,
Did he possess the power intuitive
Of diving into character. A pair
Of breeches, to his philosophic eye,
Were not what unto other folks they seem,
Mere simple breeches, but in them he saw
The symbol of the soul—mysterious, high
Hieroglyphics ! such as Egypt's Priest
Adored upon the holy Pyramid,
Vainly imagined tomb of monarchs old,
But raised by wise philosophy, that sought
By darkness to illumine, and to spread
Knowledge by dim concealment—process high
Of man's imaginative, deathless soul.
Nor, haply, in the abasement of the life
Which stern necessity had made his own,
Did he not recognize a genial power
Of soul-ennobling fortitude. He heard
Unmoved the witling's shallow contumely,
And thus, in spite of nature, by degrees
He saw a beauty and a majesty
In this despised trade, which warrior's brow
Hath rarely circled—so that when he sat
Beneath his sky-light window, he hath cast
A gaze of triumph on the godlike sun,
And felt that orb, in all his annual round,
Beheld no happier, nobler character
Than him, Hugh Thwaites, a little tailor boy.

Thus I, with no unprofitable song,
Have, in the silence of the umbrageous wood,
Chaunted the heroic youthful attributes
Of him the Flying Tailor. Much remains
Of highest argument, to lute or lyre
Fit to be murmured with impassioned voice;
And when, by timely supper and by sleep
Refreshed, I turn me to the welcome task,
With lofty hopes,—Reader, do thou expect
The final termination of my lay.
For, mark my words,—eternally my name
Shall last on earth, conspicuous like a star
'Mid that bright galaxy of favoured spirits,
Who, laughed at constantly whene'er they pub-
    lished,
Survived the impotent scorn of base Reviews,
Monthly or Quarterly, or that accursed
Journal, the Edinburgh Review, that lives
On tears, and sighs, and groans, and brains, and
    blood.

THE CHERUB

(*Coleridge*)

WAS it not lovely to behold
    A Cherub come down from the sky,
A beauteous thing of heavenly mould,
With ringlets of the wavy gold,
Dancing and floating curiously?
To see it come down to the earth,
This beauteous thing of heavenly birth!
Leaving the fields of balm and bliss,
To dwell in such a world as this!

I heard a maiden sing the while
A strain so holy, it might beguile
An angel from the radiant spheres,
That have swum in light ten thousand years;
Ten times ten thousand is too few—
Child of heaven, can this be true?
And then I saw that beauteous thing
Slowly from the clouds descending,
Brightness, glory, beauty blending,
In the mid air hovering.
It had also a halo round its head,
It was not of the rainbow's hue,
For in it was no shade of blue,
But a beam of amber mixed with red,
Like that which mingles in the ray
A little after the break of day.
Its raiment was the thousand dyes
Of flowers in the heavenly paradise;
Its track a beam of the sun refined,
And its chariot was the southern wind;
My heart danced in me with delight,
And my spirits mounted at the sight,
And I said within me, "It is well;
But where the bower, or peaceful dell,
Where this pure heavenly thing may dwell?"
Then I bethought me of the place
To lodge the messenger of grace;
And I chose the ancient sycamore,
And the little green by Greta's shore;
It is a spot so passing fair,
That sainted thing might sojourn there.

Go tell yon stranger artisan,
Build as quickly as he can.

Heaven shield us from annoy !
What shall form this dome of joy ?
The leaf of the rose would be too rude
For a thing that is not flesh and blood ;
The walls must be of the sunny air,
And the roof the silvery gossamer,
And all the ceiling, round and round,
Wove half of light, and half of sound :
The sounds must be the tones that fly
From distant harp, just ere they die ;
And the light the moon's soft midnight ray,
When the cloud is downy, and thin, and grey,
And such a bower of light and love,
Of beauty, and of harmony,
In earth below, or heaven above,
Nor mortal thing shall ever see.

The dream is past, it is gone away !
The rose is blighted on the spray :
I look behind, I look before,
The happy vision is no more !
But in its room a darker shade
Than eye hath pierced, or darkness made,
I cannot turn, yet do not know
What I would, or whither go ;
But I have heard, to heart of sin,
A small voice whispering within,
'Tis all I know, and all I trust,—
" That man is weak, but God is just."

Samuel Taylor Coleridge (1772–1834)

SONNETS ATTEMPTED IN THE MANNER OF CONTEMPORARY WRITERS

(*S. T. Coleridge*)

PENSIVE at eve on the hard world I mus'd,
  And my poor heart was sad : so at the moon
I gaz'd—and sigh'd, and sigh'd !—for, ah ! how soon
Eve darkens into night. Mine eyes perus'd
With tearful vacancy the *dampy* grass
Which wept and glitter'd in the paly ray ;
And I did pause me on my lonely way,
And mused me on those wretched ones who pass
O'er the black heath of Sorrow. But, alas !
Most of Myself I thought : when it befell
That the sooth Spirit of the breezy wood
Breath'd in mine ear—" All this is very well ;
But much of *one* thing is for *no* thing good."
Ah ! my poor heart's inexplicable swell !

ON A RUINED HOUSE IN A ROMANTIC COUNTRY

(*Chas. Lamb*)

AND this reft house is that the which he built.
  Lamented Jack ! And here his malt he pil'd,
Cautious in vain ! These rats that squeak so wild,
Squeak, not unconscious of their father's guilt.
Did ye not see her gleaming thro' the glade ?
Belike, 'twas she, the maiden all forlorn.
What though she milk no cow with crumpled horn,
Yet *aye* she haunts the dale where *erst* she stray'd ;
And *aye* beside her stalks her amorous knight !

Still on his thighs their wonted brogues are worn,
And thro' those brogues, still tatter'd and betorn,
His hindward charms gleam an unearthly white ;
As when thro' broken clouds at night's high noon
Peeps in fair fragments forth the full-orb'd harvest-
    moon !

John Leyden, M.D. (1775–1811)

THE LAY OF THE ETTERCAP
(*Imitation of a Border Ballad*)

NOW shall y tellen to ye, y wis,
    Of that Squyere hizt Ellis,
And his Dame so fre ;
So hende he is by goddes mizt,
That he nis not ymake a knizt
It is the more pitè.

He knoweth better eche glewe,
Than y can to ye shewe
Oither bi plume or greffe :
To hunte or hawke, bi frith or folde,
O play at boules in alles colde,
He is wel holden cheffe.

His eyes graye as glas ben,
And his visage alto kene,
Loveliche to paramour :
Clere as amber beth his faxe,
His face beth thin as battle-axe
That deleth dintes doure.

His witte beth both kene and sharpe,
To knizt or dame that wel can carpe
Oither in halle or boure :
And had y not that Squyere yfonde,
Y hadde ben at the se gronde,
Which had ben gret doloure.

In him y finden none nother evil,
Save that his nostril moche doth snivel,
Al throgh that vilaine snuffe :
But then his speche beth so perquire,
That those who may his carpyng here,
They never may here ynough.

His Dame beth of so meikle price,
To holden hemselves in her service,
Fele folks faine wolde be :
Soft and swote in eche steven,
Like an angel com fro heven,
Singeth sothe that fre.

I wot her carpyng bin ful queynt,
And her corps bothe smale and gent,
Semeliche to be sene :
Fete, hondes, and fingres smale,
Of perle beth eche fingre nail ;
She mizt ben Fairi Quene.

That Ladi gent wolde given a scarfe
To hym wolde kille a wreche dwarfe
Of paynim brode :
That dwarfe is a fell Ettercap,
And liven aye on nettle-sap,
And hath none nother fode.

That dwarfe he beth berdles and bare,
And weazel-blowen beth all his hair,
Lyke an ympe elfe ;
And in this middel erd all and haile
Ben no kyn thyng he loveth an dele,
Save his owen selfe.

And when the Dame ben come to toune,
That Ladi gent sall mak her boune
A selcouth feat to try,
To tak a little silver knyfe,
And end that sely dwarfes life,
And bake hym in a pye.

James Smith (1775–1839)

HAMPSHIRE FARMER'S ADDRESS
ON THE NEW DRURY LANE
(*William Cobbett*)

Most Thinking People,

 When persons address an audience from the
stage, it is usual, either in words or gesture, to say,
" Ladies and Gentlemen, your servant." If I were
base enough, mean enough, paltry enough, and
brute beast enough, to follow that fashion, I should
tell two lies in a breath. In the first place, you are
not Ladies and Gentlemen, but I hope something
better, that is to say, honest men and women ; and
in the next place, if you were ever so much ladies,
and ever so much gentlemen, I am not, *nor ever will
be*, your humble servant. You see me here, *most
thinking people*, by mere chance. I have not been

within the doors of a playhouse before for these ten
years ; nor, till that abominable custom of taking
money at the doors is discontinued, will I ever
sanction a theatre with my presence. The stage-
door is the only gate of *freedom* in the whole edifice,
and through that I made my way from Bagshaw's
in Brydges Street, to accost you. Look about you.
Are you not all comfortable ? Nay, never slink,
mun ; speak out, if you are dissatisfied, and tell me
so before I leave town. You are now, (*thanks to Mr.*
Whitbread), got into a large, comfortable house.
Not into a *gimcrack palace* ; not into a *Solomon's*
temple ; not into a frost-work of Brobdingnag
filigree ; but into a plain, honest, homely, indus-
trious, wholesome, *brown brick playhouse.* You
have been struggling for independence and elbow-
room these three years ; and who gave it you ?
Who helped you out of Lilliput ? Who routed you
from a rat-hole, five inches by four, to perch you in
a palace ? Again and again I answer, *Mr. Whit-*
bread. You might have sweltered in that place
with the Greek name till doomsday, and neither
Lord Castlereagh, Mr. Canning, no, nor the *Marquess*
Wellesley, would have turned a trowel to help you
out ! Remember that. Never forget that. Read
it to your children, and to your children's children !
And now, *most thinking people*, cast your eyes over
my head to what the builder (I beg his pardon, the
architect) calls the *proscenium.* No motto, no
slang, no popish Latin, to keep the people in the
dark. No *veluti in speculum.* Nothing in the dead
languages, properly so called, for they ought to die,
aye and be *damned* to boot ! The Covent Garden
manager tried that, and a pretty business he made of

it ! When a man says *veluti in speculum*, he is called
a man of letters. Very well, and is not a man who
cries O.P. a man of letters too ? You ran your
O.P. against his *veluti in speculum*, and pray
which beat ? I prophesied that, though I never
told any body. I take it for granted, that every
intelligent man, woman, and child, to whom I
address myself, has stood severally and respectively
in Little Russell Street, and cast their, his, her, and
its eyes on the outside of this building before they
paid their money to view the inside. Look at the
brick-work, *English Audience !* Look at the brick-
work ! All plain and smooth like a quakers' meeting. None of your Egyptian pyramids, to entomb
subscribers' capitals. No overgrown colonnades of
stone, like an alderman's gouty legs in white cotton
stockings, fit only to use as rammers for paving
Tottenham Court Road. This house is neither after
the model of a temple in Athens, no, nor a *temple
in Moorfields*, but it is built to act English plays in ;
and, provided you have good scenery, dresses, and
decorations, I daresay you wouldn't break your
hearts if the outside were as plain as the pikestaff
I used to carry when I was a sergeant. *Apropos*,
as the French valets say, who cut their masters'
throats—*apropos* a word about dresses. You must,
many of you, have seen what I have read a descrip-
tion of, Kemble and Mrs. Siddons in Macbeth, with
more gold and silver plastered on their doublets than
would have kept an honest family in butcher's meat
and flannel from year's end to year's end ! I am
informed, (now mind, I do not vouch for the fact,)
but I am informed that all such extravagant idleness
is to be done away with here. Lady Macbeth is to

have a plain quilted petticoat, a cotton gown, and a *mob cap* (as the court parasites call it ;—it will be well for them, if, one of these days, they don't wear a mob cap—I mean a *white cap*, with a *mob* to look at them) ; and Macbeth is to appear in an honest yeoman's drab coat, and a pair of black calamanco breeches. Not *Sala*manca ; no, nor *Talavera* neither, my most Noble Marquess ; but plain, honest, black calamanco stuff breeches. This is right ; this is as it should be. *Most thinking people*, I have heard you much abused. There is not a compound in the language but is strung fifty in a rope, like onions, by the Morning Post, and hurled in your teeth. You are called the mob ; and when they have made you out to be the mob, you are called the *scum* of the people, and the *dregs* of the people. I should like to know how you can be both. Take a basin of broth—not *cheap soup*, *Mr. Wilberforce*—not soup for the poor, at a penny a quart, as your mixture of horses' legs, brick-dust, and old shoes, was denominated—but plain, whole-some, patriotic beef or mutton broth ; take this, examine it, and you will find—mind, I don't vouch for the fact, but I am told—you will find the dregs at the bottom, and the scum at the top. I will endeavour to explain this to you : England is a large *earthenware pipkin* ; John Bull is the *beef* thrown into it ; taxes are the *hot water* he boils in ; rotten boroughs are the *fuel* that blazes under this same pipkin ; parliament is the *ladle* that stirs the hodge-podge, and sometimes—— But hold ! I don't wish to pay *Mr. Newman* a second visit. I leave you better off than you have been this many a day ; you have a good house over your head ; you

have beat the French in Spain ; the harvest has
turned out well ; the comet keeps its distance ; and
red slippers are hawked about in Constantinople for
next to nothing ; and for all this, *again and again*
I tell you, you are indebted to *Mr. Whitbread* ! ! !

THE THEATRE

(*Crabbe*)

'TIS sweet to view, from half-past five to six,
    Our long wax-candles, with short cotton
wicks,
Touch'd by the lamplighter's Promethean art,
Start into light, and make the lighter start ;

To see red Phœbus through the gallery-pane
Tinge with his beams the beams of Drury Lane
While gradual parties fill our widen'd pit,
And gape, and gaze, and wonder, ere they sit.

At first, while vacant seats give choice and ease,
Distant or near, they settle where they please ;
But when the multitude contracts the span,
And seats are rare, they settle where they can.

Now the full benches to late-comers doom
No room for standing, miscall'd *standing room*.
Hark ! the check-taker moody silence breaks,
And bawling " Pit full ! " gives the check he takes ;
Yet onward still the gathering numbers cram,
Contending crowders shout the frequent damn,
And all is bustle, squeeze, row, jabbering, and jam.

See to their desks Apollo's sons repair—
Swift rides the rosin o'er the horse's hair!
In unison their various tones to tune,
Murmurs the hautboy, growls the hoarse bassoon;
In soft vibrating sighs the whispering lute,
Tang goes the harpsichord, too-too the flute,
Brays the loud trumpet, squeaks the fiddle sharp,
Winds the French-horn, and twangs the tingling
    harp;
Till like great Jove, the leader, fingering in,
Attunes to order the chaotic din.
Now all seems hush'd—but, no, one fiddle will
Give half-ashamed, a tiny flourish still.
Foil'd in his crash, the leader of the clan
Reproves with frown the dilatory man:
Then on his candlestick thrice taps his bow,
Nods a new signal, and away they go.
Perchance, while pit and gallery cry, "Hats
    off!"
And awed Consumption checks his chided cough,
Some giggling daughter of the Queen of Love
Drops, 'reft of pin, her playbill from above:
Like Icarus, while laughing galleries clap,
Soars, ducks, and dives in air the printed scrap;
But, wiser far than he, combustion fears,
And, as it flies, eludes the chandeliers;
Till, sinking gradual, with repeated twirl,
It settles, curling, on a fiddler's curl;
Who from his powder'd pate the intruder strikes,
And, for mere malice, sticks it on the spikes.

Say, why these Babel strains from Babel tongues?
Who's that calls "Silence!" with such leathern
    lungs?

He who, in quest of quiet, " Silence ! " hoots,
Is apt to make the hubbub he imputes.
What various swains our motley walls contain !—
Fashion from Moorfields, honour from Chick
    Lane ;
Bankers from Paper Buildings here resort,
Bankrupts from Golden Square and Riches Court ;
From the Haymarket canting rogues in grain,
Gulls from the Poultry, sots from Water Lane ;
The lottery-cormorant, the auction shark,
The full-price master and the half-price clerk ;
Boys who long linger at the gallery door,
With pence twice five—they want but twopence
    more ;
Till some Samaritan the twopence spares,
And sends them jumping up the gallery stairs

Critics we boast who ne'er their malice balk,
But talk their minds—we wish they'd mind their
    talk ;
Big-worded bullies, who by quarrels live—
Who give the lie, and tell the lie they give ;
Jews from St. Mary Axe, for jobs so wary,
That of old clothes they'd even axe St. Mary ;
And bucks with pockets empty as their pate,
Lax in their gaiters, laxer in their gait ;
Who oft, when we our house lock up, carouse
With tippling tipstaves in a lock-up house.

Yet here, as elsewhere, Chance can joy bestow,
Where scowling Fortune seem'd to threaten woe

John Richard William Alexander Dwyer
Was footman to Justinian Stubbs, Esquire

But when John Dwyer listed in the Blues,
Emanuel Jennings polish'd Stubbs's shoes.
Emanuel Jennings brought his youngest boy
Up as a corn-cutter—a safe employ;
In Holywell Street, St. Pancras, he was bred
(At number twenty-seven, it is said),
Facing the pump, and near the Granby's Head;
He would have bound him to some shop in town,
But with a premium he could not come down.
Pat was the urchin's name, a red-hair'd youth,
Fonder of purl and skittle-grounds than truth.
Silence, ye gods! to keep your tongues in awe,
The Muse shall tell an accident she saw.

Pat Jennings in the upper gallery sat,
But, leaning forward, Jennings lost his hat:
Down from the gallery the beaver flew,
And spurn'd the one to settle in the two.

How shall he act? Pay at the gallery-door
Two shillings for what cost, when new, but four?
Or till half-price, to save his shilling, wait,
And gain his hat again at half-past eight;
Now, while his fears anticipate a thief,
John Mullins whispers, "Take my handkerchief."
"Thank you," cried Pat; "but one won't make a
    line."
"Take mine," cried Wilson; and cried Stokes,
    "Take mine."
A motley cable soon Pat Jennings ties,
Where Spitalfields with real-India vies.
Like Iris' bow, down darts the painted clue,
Starr'd, striped and spotted, yellow, red and blue
Old calico, torn silk, and muslin new.

George Green below, with palpitating hand,
Loops the last 'kerchief to the beaver's band—
Up soars the prize !   The youth, with joy unfeign'd,
Regain'd the felt, and felt what he regain'd ;
While to the applauding galleries grateful Pat
Made a low bow, and touch'd the ransom'd hat.

Horace Smith (1779–1849)

JOHNSON'S GHOST
(*Johnson*)

THAT which was organized by the moral ability of
one has been executed by the physical efforts of
many, and DRURY LANE THEATRE is now complete.
Of that part behind the curtain, which has not yet
been destined to glow beneath the brush of the
varnisher, or vibrate to the hammer of the carpenter, little is thought by the public, and little need
be said by the committee.   Truth, however, is not
to be sacrificed for the accommodation of either ;
and he who should pronounce that our edifice has
received its final embellishment would be disseminat-
ing falsehood without incurring favour, and risking
the disgrace of detection without participating the
advantage of success.

Professions lavishly effused and parsimoniously
verified are alike inconsistent with the precepts of
innate rectitude and the practice of external policy :
let it not then be conjectured, that because we are
unassuming, we are imbecile ; that forbearance is
any indication of despondency, or humility of
demerit.   He that is the most assured of success will

make the fewest appeals to favour, and where nothing is claimed that is undue, nothing that is due will be withheld. A swelling opening is too often succeeded by an insignificant conclusion. Parturient mountains have ere now produced muscipular abortions ; and the auditor who compares incipient grandeur with final vulgarity is reminded of the pious hawkers of Constantinople, who solemnly perambulate her streets, exclaiming, " In the name of the Prophet—figs ! "

Of many who think themselves wise, and of some who are thought wise by others, the exertions are directed to the revival of mouldering and obscure dramas ; to endeavours to exalt that which is now rare only because it was always worthless, and whose deterioration, while it condemned it to living obscurity, by a strange obliquity of moral perception constitutes its title to posthumous renown. To embody the flying colours of folly to arrest evanescence, to give to bubbles the globular consistency as well as form, to exhibit on the stage the piebald denizen of the stable, and the half-reasoning parent of combs, to display the brisk locomotion of Columbine, or the tortuous attitudinizing of Punch ;— these are the occupations of others, whose ambition, limited to the applause of unintellectual fatuity, is too innocuous for the application of satire, and too humble for the incitement of jealousy.

Our refectory will be found to contain every species of fruit, from the cooling nectarine and luscious peach to the puny pippin and the noxious nut. There Indolence may repose, and Inebriety revel ; and the spruce apprentice, rushing in at second account, may there chatter with impunity ;

debarred, by a barrier of brick and mortar, from marring that scenic interest in others, which nature and education have disqualified him from comprehending himself.

Permanent stage-doors we have none. That which is permanent cannot be removed, for, if removed, it soon ceases to be permanent. What stationary absurdity can vie with that ligneous barricado, which, decorated with frappant and tintinnabulant appendages, now serves as the entrance of the lowly cottage, and now as the exit of a lady's bed-chamber; at one time, insinuating plastic Harlequin into a butcher's shop, and, at another, yawning, as a flood-gate, to precipitate the Cyprians of St. Giles's into the embraces of Macheath. To elude this glaring absurdity, to give to each respective mansion the door which the carpenter would doubtless have given, we vary our portal with the varying scene, passing from deal to mahogany, and from mahogany to oak, as the opposite claims of cottage, palace, or castle, may appear to require.

Amid the general hum of gratulation which flatters us in front, it is fit that some regard should be paid to the murmurs of despondence that assail us in the rear. They, as I have elsewhere expressed it, " who live to please," should not have their own pleasures entirely overlooked. The children of Thespis are general in their censures of the architect, in having placed the locality of exit at such a distance from the oily irradiators which now dazzle the eyes of him who addresses you. I am, cries the Queen of Terrors, robbed of my fair proportions. When the king-killing Thane hints to the breathless auditory the murders he means to perpetrate, in the castle of Macduff, ere his purpose cool, so vast is the interval he has to travel before he can escape from the stage, that his purpose has even time to freeze. Your condition, cries the Muse of Smiles, is hard, but it is cygnet's down in comparison with mine. The peerless peer of capers and congees has laid it down as a rule, that the best good thing uttered by the morning visitor should conduct him rapidly to the doorway, last impressions vying in durability with first. But when, on this boarded elongation, it falls to my lot to say a good thing, to ejaculate, "keep moving," or to chant, "*hic hoc horum genitivo*," many are the moments that must elapse, ere I can hide myself from public vision in the recesses of O.P. or P.S.

To objections like these, captiously urged and querulously maintained, it is time that equity should conclusively reply. Deviation from scenic propriety has only to vituperate itself for the consequences it generates. Let the actor consider the line of exit as that line beyond which he should not soar in quest of spurious applause : let him reflect, that in proportion as he advances to the lamps, he recedes from nature ; that the truncheon of Hotspur acquires no additional charm from encountering the cheek of beauty in the stage-box, and that the bravura of Mandane may produce effect, although the throat of her who warbles it should not overhang the orchestra. The Jove of the modern critical Olympus, Lord Mayor of the theatric sky, has *ex cathedra* asserted, that a natural actor looks upon the audience part of the theatre as the third side of the chamber he inhabits. Surely, of the third wall

thus fancifully erected, our actors should, by ridicule
or reason, be withheld from knocking their heads
against the stucco.

Time forcibly reminds me, that all things which
have a limit must be brought to a conclusion.   Let
me, ere that conclusion arrives, recall to your recol-
lection, that the pillars which rise on either side of
me, blooming in virid antiquity, like two massy
evergreens, had yet slumbered in their native
quarry, but for the ardent exertions of the individual
who called them into life : to his never-slumbering
talents you are indebted for whatever pleasure this
haunt of the muses is calculated to afford.   If, in
defiance of chaotic malevolence, the destroyer of the
temple of Diana yet survives in the name of Erostra-
tus, surely we may confidently predict, that the
rebuilder of the temple of Apollo will stand recorded
to distant posterity in that of—SAMUEL WHIT-
BREAD.

A TALE OF DRURY LANE

(*Scott*)

SURVEY this shield, all bossy bright—
    These cuisses twain behold !
Look on my form in armour dight
Of steel inlaid with gold ;
My knees are stiff in iron buckles,
Stiff spikes of steel protect my knuckles.
These once belong'd to sable prince,
Who never did in battle wince ;
With valour tart as pungent quince,
He slew the vaunting Gaul.

Rest there awhile, my bearded lance,
While from green curtain I advance
To yon footlights, no trivial dance,
And tell the town what sad mischance
Did Drury Lane befall.

THE NIGHT

On fair Augusta's towers and trees
Flitted the silent midnight breeze,
Curling the foliage as it past,
Which from the moon-tipp'd plumage cast
A spangled light, like dancing spray,
Then reassumed its still array ;
When, as night's lamp unclouded hung,
And down its full effulgence flung,
It shed such soft and balmy power
That cot and castle, hall and bower,
And spire and dome, and turret height,
Appear'd to slumber in the light.
From Henry's chapel, Rufus' hall,
To Savoy, Temple, and St. Paul,
From Knightsbridge, Pancras, Camden Town,
To Redriff, Shadwell, Horsleydown,
No voice was heard, no eye unclosed,
But all in deepest sleep reposed.
They might have thought, who gazed around
Amid a silence so profound,
    It made the senses thrill,
That 'twas no place inhabited,
But some vast city of the dead—
    All was so hush'd and still.

THE BURNING

As Chaos, which, by heavenly doom,
Had slept in everlasting gloom,

Started with terror and surprise
When light first flashed upon her eyes——
So London's sons in nightcap woke,
    In bedgown woke her dames ;
For shouts were heard 'mid fire and smoke,
And twice ten hundred voices spoke—
    " The playhouse is in flames ! "
And lo ! where Catherine Street extends,
A fiery tail its lustre lends
    To every window-pane ;
Blushes each spout in Martlet Court,
And Barbican, moth-eaten fort,
And Covent Garden kennels sport,
    A bright ensanguined drain ;
Meux's new brewhouse shows the light,
Rowland Hill's chapel, and the height
    Where patent shot they sell ;
The Tennis Court, so fair and tall,
Partakes the ray, with Surgeons' Hall,
The ticket-porters' house of call,
Old Bedlam, close by London Wall,
    And Richardson's Hotel.
Nor these alone, but far and wide,
Across red Thames's gleaming tide,
To distant fields, the blaze was borne,
And daisy white and hoary thorn
In borrow'd lustre seem'd to sham
The rose or red Sweet Wil-li-am.
To those who on the hills around
Beheld the flames from Drury's mound,
    As from a lofty altar rise,
It seem'd that nations did conspire
To offer to the god of fire
    Some vast stupendous sacrifice !

The summon'd firemen woke at call,
And hied them to their stations all:
Starting from short and broken snooze,
Each sought his pond'rous hobnailed shoes,
But first his worsted hosen plied,
Plush breeches next, in crimson dyed,
   His nether bulk embraced;
Then jacket thick, of red or blue,
Whose massy shoulder gave to view
The badge of each respective crew,
   In tin or copper traced.
The engines thunder'd through the street,
Fire-hook, pipe, bucket, all complete,
And torches glared, and clattering feet
   Along the pavement paced.
And one, the leader of the band,
From Charing Cross along the Strand,
Like stag by beagles hunted hard,
Ran till he stopp'd at Vin'gar Yard.
The burning badge his shoulder bore,
The belt and oilskin hat he wore,
The cane he had, his men to bang,
Show'd foreman of the British gang—
His name was Higginbottom. Now
'Tis meet that I should tell you how
   The others came in view:
The Hand-in-Hand the race began,
Then came the Phœnix and the Sun,
Th' Exchange, where old insurers run,
   The Eagle, where the new;
With these came Runford, Bumford, Cole,
Robins from Hockly in the Hole,
Lawson and Dawson, cheek by jowl,
   Crump from St. Giles's Pound:

Whitford and Mitford join'd the train,
Huggins and Muggins from Chick Lane,
And Clutterbuck, who got a sprain
    Before the plug was found.
Hobson and Jobson did not sleep,
But ah! no trophy could they reap,
For both were in the Donjon Keep
    Of Bridewell's gloomy mound!
E'en Higginbottom now was posed,
For sadder scene was ne'er disclosed;
Without, within, in hideous show,
Devouring flames resistless glow,
And blazing rafters downward go,
And never halloo "Heads below!"
    Nor notice give at all.
The firemen terrified are slow
To bid the pumping torrent flow,
    For fear the roof should fall.
Back, Robins, back! Crump, stand aloof;
    Whitford, keep near the walls!
Huggins, regard your own behoof,
For, lo! the blazing rocking roof
    Down, down, in thunder falls!
An awful pause succeeds the stroke,
And o'er the ruin's volumed smoke,
Rolling around its pitchy shroud,
Conceal'd them from th' astonished crowd.
At length the mist awhile was clear'd,
When, lo! amid the wreck uprear'd,
Gradual a moving head appear'd,
    And Eagle firemen knew
'Twas Joseph Muggins, name revered,
    The foreman of their crew.
Loud shouted all in signs of woe,

"A Muggins! to the rescue, ho!"
    And pour'd the hissing tide;
Meanwhile the Muggins fought amain,
And strove and struggled all in vain,
For, rallying but to fall again,
    He totter'd, sunk, and died!
Did none attempt, before he fell,
To succour one they loved so well?
Yes, Higginbottom did aspire
(His fireman's soul was all on fire)
    His brother chief to save;
But ah! his reckless generous ire
    Served but to share his grave!
'Mid blazing beams and scalding streams,
Through fire and smoke he dauntless broke
    Where Muggins broke before.
But sulphury stench and boiling drench
Destroying sight o'erwhelmed him quite,
    He sunk to rise no more.
Still o'er his head, while Fate he braved,
His whizzing water-pipe he waved;
"Whitford and Mitford, ply your pumps,
You, Clutterbuck, come, stir your stumps,
Why are you in such doleful dumps?
A fireman, and afraid of bumps!—
What are they fear'd on? fools, 'od rot 'em!"
Were the last words of Higginbottom.

THE REVIVAL

Peace to his soul! new prospects bloom,
And toil rebuilds what fires consume!
Eat we and drink we, be our ditty,
"Joy to the managing committee!"

Eat we and drink we, join to rum
Roast beef and pudding of the plum ;
Forth from thy nook, John Horner, come,
With bread of ginger brown thy thumb,
    For this is Drury's gay day :
Roll, roll thy hoop, and twirl thy tops,
And buy, to glad thy smiling chops,
Crisp parliament with lolly-pops,
    And fingers of the Lady.

Didst mark, how toil'd the busy train,
From morn to eve, till Drury Lane
Leap'd like a roebuck from the plain ?
Ropes rose and stooped, and rose again,
    And nimble workmen trod ;
To realize bold Wyatt's plan
Rush'd many a howling Irishman ;
Loud clatter'd many a porter-can,
And many a raggamuffin clan,
    With trowel and with hod.

Drury revives ! her rounded pate
Is blue, is heavenly blue with slate ;
She " wings the midway air," elate,
    As magpie, crow, or chough ;
White paint her modish visage smears,
Yellow and pointed are her ears.
No pendent portico appears
Dangling beneath, for Whitebread's shears
    Have cut the bauble off.

Yet, she exalts her stately head ;
And, but that solid bulk outspread
A.P.   E

Opposed you on your onward tread,
And posts and pillars warranted
That all was true that Wyatt said,
You might have deemed her walls so thick
Were not composed of stone or brick,
But all a phantom, all a trick,
Of brain disturb'd and fancy sick,
So high she soars, so vast, so quick !

THE LIVING LUSTRES

(*Thomas Moore*)

I

O WHY should our dull retrospective addresses
    Fall damp as wet blankets on Drury Lane
    fire?
Away with blue devils, away with distresses,
    And give the gay spirit to sparkling desire !

II

Let the artists decide on the beauties of Drury,
    The richest to me is when woman is there ;
The question of houses I leave to the jury,
    The fairest to me is the house of the fair.

III

When woman's soft smile all our senses bewilders,
    And gilds, while it carves, her dear form on the
    heart,
What need has New Drury of carvers and gilders ?
    With Nature so bounteous, why call upon
    Art ?

IV

How well would our actors attend to their duties,
  Our house save in oil, and our authors in wit,
In lieu of yon lamps, if a row of young beauties
  Glanced light from their eyes between us and the
    pit !

V

The apples that grew on the fruit-tree of knowledge
  By woman were pluck'd, and she still wears the
    prize,
To tempt us in theatre, senate, or college—
  I mean the love-apples that bloom in the eyes.

VI

There too is the lash which, all statutes controlling,
  Still governs the slaves that are made by the
    fair ;
For man is the pupil, who, while her eye's rolling,
  Is lifted to rapture, or sunk in despair.

VII

Bloom, theatre, bloom, in the roseate blushes
  Of beauty illumed by a love-breathing smile !
And flourish, ye pillars, as green as the rushes
  That pillow the nymphs of the Emerald Isle !

VIII

For dear is the Emerald Isle of the ocean,
  Whose daughters are fair as the foam of the wave,
Whose sons, unaccustom'd to rebel commotion,
  Tho' joyous, are sober—tho' peaceful, are brave.

IX

The shamrock their olive, sworn foe to a quarrel;
  Protects from the thunder and lightning of rows;
Their sprig of shillelagh is nothing but laurel,
  Which flourishes rapidly over their brows.

X

Oh! soon shall they burst the tyrannical shackles
  Which each panting bosom indignantly names,
Until not one goose at the capital cackles
  Against the grand question of Catholic claims.

XI

And then shall each Paddy, who once on the Liffey
  Perchance held the helm of some mackerel hoy,
Hold the helm of the state, and dispense in a jiffy
  More fishes than ever he caught when a boy.

XII

And those who now quit their hods, shovels, and
    barrows,
  In crowds to the bar of some ale-house to flock,
When bred to *our* bar shall be Gibbses and Garrows,
  Assume the silk gown, and discard the smock-
    frock.

XIII

For Erin surpasses the daughters of Neptune,
  As Dian outshines each encircling star;
And the spheres of the heavens could never have
    kept tune
  Till set to the music of Erin-go-bragh.

Thomas Love Peacock (1785–1886)

SONG BY MR. CYPRESS

(Byron)

THERE is a fever of the spirit,
  The brand of Cain's unresting doom,
Which in the lone dark souls that bear it
  Glows like the lamp in Tullia's tomb.
Unlike the lamp, its subtle fire
  Burns, blasts, consumes its cell, the heart.
Till, one by one, hope, joy, desire,
  Like dreams of shadowy smoke depart.

When hope, love, life itself, are only
  Dust—spectral memories—dead and cold—
The unfed fire burns bright and lonely,
  Like that undying lamp of old ;
And by that drear illumination,
  Till time its clay-built home has rent,
Thought broods on feeling's desolation—
  The soul is its own monument.

William Maginn (1793–1842)

THE GALIONGEE

(Byron)

THE Pasha sat in his divan,
  With silver-sheathed ataghan ;
And called to him a Galiongee,
Come lately from the Euxine Sea

To Stamboul; chains were on his feet,
  And fetters on his hands were seen,
  Because he was a Nazarene:
When duly making reverence meet,
With haughty glance on that divan,
And curling lip he thus began:

" By broad Phingari's silver light
When sailing at the noon of night,
Bismillah! whom did we descry
  But dark corsairs, who, bent on spoil,
  Athwart the deep sea ever toil!
We knew their blood-red flags on high:
The Captain he called, belike,
With gesture proud, to bid us strike,
And told his Sonbachis to spare
Of not one scalp a single hair,
Though garbs of green showed Emirs there!
It boots not, Pasha, to relate
  What souls were sent to Eblis throne
How Azrael's arrows scattered fate,
  How wild, wet, wearied, and alone
When all my crew were drenched in blood,
Or floated lifeless on the flood,
I fought unawed, nor e'er thought I
To shout ' Amaun!' the craven's cry,
  I took my handkerchief to wipe
My burning brow, and then I took,
With placid hand, my long Chibouque,
  That is to say, my Turkish pipe,
And having clapped it in my cheek
Disdaining e'er a word to speak
I shouted to the pirate, ' Now,
You've fairly beat me, I allow '," etc.

John Keats (1795–1821)

A PORTRAIT
(E. *Spenser*)

H E is to meet a melancholy carle :
    Thin in the waist, with bushy head of hair,
As hath the seeded thistle, when a parle
It holds with Zephyr, ere it sendeth fair
Its light balloons into the summer air ;
Thereto his beard had not begun to bloom.
No brush had touched his cheek, or razor shear ;
No care had touched his cheek with mortal doom,
But new he was and bright, as scarf from Persian
    loom.
Ne caréd he for wine, or half and half ;
Ne caréd he for fish, or flesh, or fowl ;
And sauces held he worthless as the chaff ;
He's deigned the swine-head at the wassail-bowl ;
Ne with lewd ribbalds sat he cheek by jowl ;
Ne with sly lemans in the scorner's chair ;
But after water-brooks this pilgrim's soul
Panted and all his food was woodland air ;
Though he would oft-times feast on gilliflowers rare.

The slang of cities in no wise he knew,
Tipping the wink to him was heathen Greek ;
He sipped no " olden Tom ", or " ruin blue ",
Or Nantz, or cherry-brandy, drank full meek
By many a damsel brave and rouge of cheek ;
Nor did he know each agéd watchman's beat,—
Nor in obscuréd purlieus would he seek,
For curléd Jewesses, with ankles neat,
Who, as they walk abroad, made twinkling with
    their feet.

John Hamilton Reynolds
(1796–1852)

PETER BELL : A LYRICAL BALLAD
(*Wordsworth*)

I

IT is the thirty-first of March,
  A gusty evening—half-past seven ;
The moon is shining o'er the larch,
A simple shape—a cock'd-up arch,
Rising bigger than a star,
Though the stars are thick in Heaven.

II

Gentle Moon ! How canst thou shine
Over graves and over trees,
With as innocent a look
As my own grey eyeball sees,
When I gaze upon a brook ?

III

Od's me ! how the moon doth shine :
It doth make a pretty glitter,
Playing in the waterfall ;
As when Lucy Gray doth litter
Her baby-house with bugles small.

IV

Beneath the ever blessed moon
An old man o'er an old grave stares,
You never look'd upon his fellow ;
His brow is covered with grey hairs,
As though they were an umbrella.

V

He hath a noticeable look,
This old man hath—this grey old man ;
He gazes at the graves, and seems,
With over waiting, over wan,
Like Susan Harvey's pan of creams.

VI

'Tis Peter Bell—'tis Peter Bell,
Who never stirreth in the day ;
His hand is wither'd—he is old !
On Sundays he is us'd to pray,
In winter he is very cold.

VII

I've seen him in the month of August,
At the wheatfield, hour by hour,
Picking ear,—by ear—by ear,—
Through wind,—and rain,—and sun,—and shower
From year,—to year,—to year,—to year.

VIII

You never saw a wiser man,
He knows his Numeration Table ;
He counts the sheep of Harry Gill,
Every night that he is able,
When the sheep are on the hill.

IX

Betty Foy—My Betty Foy,
Is the aunt of Peter Bell ;
And credit me, as I would have you,
Simon Lee was once his nephew.
And his niece is Alice Fell.

X

He is rurally related ;
Peter Bell hath country cousins,
(He had once a worthy mother)
Bells and Peters by the dozens,
But Peter Bell he hath no brother.

XI

Not a brother owneth he,
Peter Bell he hath no brother,
His mother had no other son,
No other son e'er call'd her mother ;
Peter Bell hath brother none.

XII

Hark ! the churchyard brook is singing
Its evening song amid the leaves ;
And the peering moon doth look
Sweetly on that singing brook,
Round and sad as though it grieves.

XIII

The little leaves on long thin twigs
Tremble with a deep delight,
They do dance a pleasant rout,
Hop and skip and jump about
As though they all were craz'd to-night.

XIV

Peter Bell doth lift his hand,
That thin hand, which in the light
Looketh like to oiled paper ;
Paper oiled,—oily bright,—
And held up to a waxen taper.

XV

The hand of Peter Bell is busy,
Under the pent-house of his hairs ;
His eye is like a solemn sermon ;
The little flea severely fares,
'Tis a sad day for the vermin.

XVI

He is thinking of the Bible—
Peter Bell is old and blest ;
He doth pray and scratch away,
He doth scratch, and bitten, pray
To *flee* away, and be at rest.

XVII

At home his foster child is cradled—
Four brown bugs are feeding there ;
Catch as many, sister Ann,
Catch as many as you can,
And yet the little insects spare.

XVIII

Why should blessed insects die ?
The flea doth skip o'er Betty Foy,
Like a little living thing ;
Though it hath not fin or wing,
Hath it not a moral joy ?

XIX

I the poet of the mountain,
Of the waterfall and fell,
I the mighty mental medlar,
I the lonely lyric pedlar,
I the Jove of Alice Fell.

XX

I the Recluse—a gentle man,
A gentle man—a simple creature,
Who would not hurt, God shield the thing,
The merest, meanest May-bug's wing,
Am tender in my tender nature.

XXI

I do doat on my dear wife,
On the linnet, on the worm,
I can see sweet written salads
Growing in the Lyric Ballads,
And always find them green and firm.

XXII

Peter Bell is laughing now,
Like a dead man making faces;
Never saw I smile so old,
On face so wrinkled and so cold,
Since the idiot Boy's grimaces.

XXIII

He is thinking of the moors,
Where I saw him in his breeches;
Ragged though they were, a pair
Fit for a grey old man to wear;
Saw him poking—gathering leeches.

XXIV

And gather'd leeches are to him,
To Peter Bell, like gather'd flowers;
They do yield him such delight,
As roses poach'd from porch at night,
Or pluck'd from oratoric bowers.

XXV

How that busy smile doth hurry
O'er the cheek of Peter Bell;
He is surely in a flurry,
Hurry skurry—hurry skurry,
Such delight I may not tell.

XXVI

His stick is made of wilding wood,
His hat was formerly of felt,
His duffel cloak of wool is made,
His stockings are from stock in trade,
His belly's belted with a belt.

XXVII

His father was a bellman once,
His mother was a beldame old;
They kept a shop at Keswick Town,
Close by the Bell, (beyond the Crown),
And pins and peppermint they sold.

XXVIII

He is stooping now about
O'er the gravestones one and two;
The clock is now a-striking eight,
Four more hours and 'twill be late,
And Peter Bell hath much to do.

XXIX

O'er the gravestones three and four,
Peter stoopeth old and wise;
He counteth with a wizard glee
The graves of all his family,
While the hooting owlet cries.

XXX

Peter Bell, he readeth ably,
All his letters he can tell ;
Roman W,—Roman S,
In a minute he can guess,
Without the aid of Dr. Bell.

XXXI

Peter keeps a gentle poney,
But the poney is not here ;
Susan who is very tall,
And very sick and sad withal,
Rides it slowly far and near.

XXXII

Hark ! the voice of Peter Bell,
And the belfry bell is knelling ;
It soundeth drowsily and dead,
As though a corse th' " Excursion " read ;
Or Martha Ray her tale was telling.

XXXIII

Do listen unto Peter Bell,
While your eyes with tears do glisten—
Silence ! his old eyes do read
All, on which the boys do tread
When holidays do come—Do listen !

XXXIV

The ancient Marinere lieth here,
Never to rise, although he pray'd,—
But all men, all, must have their fallings ;
And, like the Fear of Mr. Collins,
He died " of sounds himself had made ".

XXXV

Dead mad mother,—Martha Ray,
Old Matthew too, and Betty Foy,
Lack-a-daisy! here's a rout full;
Simon Lee whose age was doubtful,
Simon even the Fates destroy.

XXXVI

Harry Gill is gone to rest,
Goody Blake is food for maggot;
They lie sweetly side by side,
Beautiful as when they died;
Never more shall she pick faggot.

XXXVII

Still he reads, and still the moon
On the churchyard's mounds doth shine;
The brook is still demurely singing,
Again the belfrey bell is ringing.
'Tis nine o'clock, six, seven, eight, nine!

XXXVIII

Patient Peter pores and proses
On, from simple grave to grave;
Here marks the children snatch'd to heaven,
None left to blunder " we are seven ";—
Even Andrew Jones no power could save.

XXXIX

What a Sexton's work is here,
Lord! the Idiot Boy is gone;
And Barbara Lewthwaite's fate the same,
And cold as mutton is her lamb;
And Alice Fell is bone by bone.

XL

Stephen Hill is dead and buried.
Reginald Shore is crumbling—crumbling,
Giles Fleming—Susan Gale—alas !
Death playeth in the churchyard grass
His human nine-pins—tumbling—tumbling.

XLI

But Peter liveth well and wisely,
For still he makes old Death look silly,
Like those sage ducks of Mrs. Bond,
Who, not of killing over fond,
Turn a deaf ear to dilly, dilly.

XLII

And tears are thick with Peter Bell,
Yet still he sees one blessed tomb ;
Tow'rds it he creeps with spectacles,
And bending on his leather knees,
He reads the *Lakeiest* Poet's doom.

XLIII

The letters printed are by fate,
The death they say was suicide ;
He reads—" Here lieth W.W.
Who never more will trouble you, trouble you " ;
The old man smokes who 'tis that died.

XLIV

Go home, go home—old man, go home ;
Peter, lay thee down at night,
Thou art happy, Peter Bell,
Say thy prayers for Alice Fell,
Thou hast seen a blessed sight.

XLV

He quits that moonlight yard of skulls,
And still he feels right glad, and smiles
With moral joy at that old tomb ;
Peter's cheek recalls its bloom,
And as he creepeth by the tiles,
He mutters ever—" W.W.
Never more will trouble you, trouble you."

Hartley Coleridge (1796–1849)

HE LIVED AMIDST TH' UNTRODDEN WAYS

(*Wordsworth*)

HE lived amidst th' untrodden ways
   To Rydal Lake that lead ;
A bard whom there were none to praise,
   And very few to read.

Behind a cloud his mystic sense,
   Deep hidden, who can spy ?
Bright as the night when not a star
   Is shining in the sky.

Unread his works—his " Milk White Doe "
   With dust is dark and dim ;
It's still in Longmans' shop, and oh !
   The difference to him !

Thomas Hood, the Elder (1799–1845)

HUGGINS AND DUGGINS
(*Pope*)

TWO swains or clowns—but call them swains—
　　While keeping flocks on Salisbury Plains,
For all that tend on sheep as drovers,
Are turned to songsters, or to lovers,
Each of the lass he call'd his dear
Began to carol loud and clear.
First Huggins sang, and Duggins then,
In the way of ancient shepherd men ;
Who thus alternate hitch'd in song,
" All things by turns, and nothing long."

HUGGINS

Of all the girls about our place,
There's one beats all in form and face ;
Search through all Great and Little Bumpstead
You'll only find one Peggy Plumstead.

DUGGINS

To groves and streams I tell my flame ;
I make the cliffs repeat her name :
When I'm inspired by gills and noggins,
The rocks re-echo Sally Hoggins !

HUGGINS

When I am walking in the grove,
I think of Peggy as I rove.
I'd carve her name on every tree,
But I don't know my A, B, C.

DUGGINS

Whether I walk in hill or valley,
I think of nothing else but Sally.

I'd sing her praise, but I can sing
No song, except " God save the King ".

HUGGINS

My Peggy does all nymphs excel,
And all confess she bears the bell,—
Where'er she goes swains flock together,
Like sheep that follow the bell-wether.

DUGGINS

Sally is tall and not too straight,—
Those very poplar shapes I hate ;
But something twisted like an S,—
A crook becomes a shepherdess.

HUGGINS

When Peggy's dog her arms emprison,
I often wish my lot was hisn ;
How often I should stand and turn,
To get a pat from hands like hern.

DUGGINS

I tell Sall's lambs how blest they be,
To stand about and stare at she ;
But when I look, she turns and shies,
And won't bear none but their sheep's-eyes !

HUGGINS

Love goes with Peggy where she goes,—
Beneath her smile the garden grows ;
Potatoes spring, and cabbage starts,
'Tatoes have eyes, and cabbage hearts !

DUGGINS

Where Sally goes it's always Spring,
Her presence brightens everything ;
The sun smiles bright, but where her grin is,
It makes brass farthings look like guineas.

HUGGINS

For Peggy I can have no joy,
She's sometimes kind, and sometimes coy,
And keeps me, by her wayward tricks,
As comfortless as sheep with ticks.

DUGGINS

Sally is ripe as June or May,
And yet as cold as Christmas day ;
For when she's asked to change her lot,
Lamb's wool,—but Sally, she wool not.

HUGGINS

Only with Peggy and with health,
I'd never wish for state or wealth ;
Talking of having health and more pence,
I'd drink her health if I had fourpence.

DUGGINS

Oh, how that day would seem to shine,
If Sally's banns were read with mine ;
She cries, when such a wish I carry,
" Marry come up ! " but will not marry.

ODE ON A DISTANT PROSPECT OF CLAPHAM
ACADEMY
(*T. Gray*)

AH me ! those old familiar bounds !
    That classic house, those classic grounds,
  My pensive thought recalls !
What tender urchins now confine,
What little captives now repine,
  Within yon irksome walls ?

Ay, that's the very house! I know
Its ugly windows, ten a-row!
  Its chimneys in the rear!
And there's the iron rod so high,
That drew the thunder from the sky,
  And turn'd our table-beer!

There I was birch'd! there I was bred!
There like a little Adam fed
  From Learning's woeful tree!
The weary tasks I used to con!—
The hopeless leaves I wept upon!—
  Most fruitless leaves to me!—

The summon'd class!—the awful bow!—
I wonder who is master now
  And wholesome anguish sheds!
How many ushers now employs,
How many maids to see the boys
  Have nothing in their heads!

And Mrs. S*** ?—Doth she abet
(Like Pallas in the parlour) yet
  Some favour'd two or three,—
The little Crichtons of the hour,
Her muffin-medals that devour,
  And swill her prize—bohea?

Ay, there's the play-ground! there's the lime
Beneath whose shade in summer's prime
  So wildly I have read!—
Who sits there *now*, and skims the cream
Of young Romance, and weaves a dream
  Of Love and Cottage-bread?

Who struts the Randall of the walk?
Who models tiny heads in chalk?
  Who scoops the light canoe?
What early genius buds apace?
Where's Poynter? Harris? Bowers? Chase?
  Hal Baylis? blithe Carew?

Alack! they're gone—a thousand ways!
And some are serving in "the Greys",
  And some have perish'd young!—
Jack Harris weds his second wife;
Hal Baylis drives the *wane* of life;
  And blithe Carew—is hung!

Grave Bowers teaches A B C
To savages at Owhyee;[1]
  Poor Chase is with the worms!—
All, all are gone—the olden breed!—
New crops of mushroom boys succeed,
  And push us from our *forms*!

Lo! where they scramble forth, and shout,
And leap, and skip, and mob about,
  At play where we have play'd!
Some hop, some run (some fall), some twine
Their crony arms; some in the shine,
  And some are in the shade!

Lo! there what mix'd conditions run!
The orphan lad; the widow's son;
  And Fortune's favour'd care—
The wealthy-born, for whom she hath
Mac-Adamized the future path—
  The Nabob's pamper'd heir!

---

[1] The earlier form of Hawaii.

Some brightly star'd—some evil born,—
For honour some, and some for scorn,—
  For fair or foul renown !
Good, bad, indiff'rent—none may lack !
Look, here's a White, and there's a Black !
  And there's a Creole brown !

Some laugh and sing, some mope and weep,
And wish *their* frugal sires would keep
  Their only sons at home ;—
Some tease the future tense, and plan
The full-grown doings of the man,
  And pant for years to come !

A foolish wish ! There's one at hoop ;
And four at *fives* ! and five who stoop
  The marble taw to speed !
And one that curvets in and out,
Reining his fellow Cob about,—
  Would I were in his *steed* !

Yet he would gladly halt and drop
That boyish harness off, to swop
  With this world's heavy van—
To toil, to tug. O little fool !
Whilst thou canst be a horse at school
  To wish to be a man !

Perchance thou deem'st it were a thing
To wear a crown,—to be a king !
  And sleep on regal down !
Alas ! thou know'st not kingly cares ;
Far happier is thy head that wear
  That hat without a crown !

And dost thou think that years acquire
New added joys? Dost think thy sire
   More happy than his son?
That manhood's mirth?—Oh, go thy ways
To Drury Lane when — *plays*,
   And see how *forced* our fun!

Thy taws are brave!—thy tops are rare!—
Our tops are spun with coils of care,
   Our *dumps* are no delight!—
The Elgin marbles are but tame,
And 'tis at best a sorry game
   To fly the Muse's kite!

Our hearts are dough, our heels are lead,
Our topmost joys fall dull and dead
   Like balls with no rebound!
And often with a faded eye
We look behind, and send a sigh
   Towards that merry ground!

Then be contented. Thou hast got
The most of heav'n in thy young lot,
   There's sky-blue in thy cup!
Thou'lt find thy Manhood all too fast—
Soon come, soon gone! and Age at last
   A sorry *breaking up*!

William Edmondstoune Aytoun
(1813–1865) and
Sir Theodore Martin (1815–1909)

EASTERN SERENADE

THE minarets wave on the plains of Stamboul,
 And the breeze of the evening blows freshly
 and cool ;
The voice of the musnud is heard from the west,
And kaftan and kalpac have gone to their rest.
The notes of the kislar re-echo no more,
And the waves of Al Sirat fall light on the shore.

Where art thou, my beauty : where art thou, my
 bride ?
Oh, come and repose by thy dragoman's side !
I wait for thee still by the flowery tophaik—
I have broken my eiblis for Zuleima's sake.
But the heart that adores thee is faithful and true,
Though it beats, 'neath the folds of a Greek Allah-hu !

Oh, wake thee, my dearest ! the muftis are still,
And the tshocadars sleep on the Frabgestan hill ;
No sullen aleikoum—no derveesh is here,
And the mosques are all watching by lonely Kash-
 mere !
Oh, come in the gush of thy beauty so full,
I have waited for thee, my adored attar-gul !

I see thee—I hear thee—thy antelope foot
Treads lightly and softly on the velvet cheroot ;

The jewelled amaun of thy zenzem is bare,
And the folds of thy palampore wave in the air,
Come, rest on the bosom that loves thee so well,
My dove ! my phingari ! my gentle gazelle !

Nay, tremble not, dearest !   I feel thy heart throb
'Neath the sheltering shroud of thy snowy kiebaub ;
Lo, there shines Muezzin, the beautiful star !
Thy lover is with thee, and danger afar :
Say, is it the glance of the haughty vizier,
Or the bark of the distant effendi, you fear ?

Oh, swift fly the hours in the garden of bliss !
And sweeter than balm of Gehenna, thy kiss !
Wherever I wander—wherever I roam,
My spirit flies back to its beautiful home :
It dwells by the lake of the limpid Stamboul,
With thee, my adored one ! my own attar-gul !

Shirley Brooks (1816–1874)

MORE LUCK TO HONEST POVERTY
(*Robert Burns*)

MORE luck to honest poverty,
     It claims respect, and a' that ;
But honest wealth's a better thing,
     We dare be rich for a' that.
       For a' that, and a' that,
         And spooney cant and a' that,
       A man may have a ten-pun note,
         And be a brick for a' that.

What though on soup and fish we dine,
  Wear evening togs and a' that,
A man may like good meat and wine
  Nor be a knave for a' that.
    For a' that, and a' that,
      Their fustian talk and a' that,
    A gentleman, however clean,
      May have a heart for a' that.

A prince can make a belted knight,
  A marquis, duke and a' that,
And if the title's earned, all right,
  Old England's fond of a' that.
    For a' that, and a' that,
      Their balderdash and a' that,
    A name that tells of service done,
      Is worth the wear for a' that.

Then let us pray that come it may,
  And come it will for a' that,
That common sense may take the place
  Of common cant and a' that.
    For a' that, and a' that,
      Who cackles trash and a' that,
    Or be he lord, or be he low,
      The man's an ass for a' that.

Charles Godfrey Leland (1824–1903)

TOP-SIDE GALOW

(*Longfellow—Excelsior*)

THAT nightey-tim begin chop-chop
    One young man walkey, no can stop,
Maskee snow, maskee ice,
He cally flag with chop so nice
    Top-side galow !

He muchee solly—one piecee eye
Look-see sharp—so—all-same my,
He talkey largey—talkee stlong,
Too muchee curio—all-same gong,
    Top-side galow !

Inside house he can see light,
And evely loom got fire all light,
He lookee plenty ice more high
Insidee mouth he plenty cly,
    Top-side galow !

Old man talkee, " No can walk,
By'mby lain come—velly dark
Hab got water, velly wide,"
Maskee, my must go top-side,
    Top-side galow !

" Man-man," one girley talkee he,
" What for you go top-side look-see ? "
And one tim more he plenty cly,
But 'allo-tim walkee plenty high,
    Top-side galow !

" Take care t'hat spoilum t*l*ee, young man,
Take care t'hat ice. He want man-man."
T'hat coolie chin-chin he, " Good-night ! "
He talkee my can go all *l*ight
   Top-side galow !

Joss-pidgin-man he soon begin
Morning-tim t'hat Joss chin-chin.
He no man see, him plenty fear,
Cos some man talkee he can hear
   Top-side galow !

T'hat young man die, one large dog see
Too muchee bobbe*l*y findee he.
He hand blong colo—all-same ice,
Hab got he flag with chop so nice,
   Top-side galow !

MORAL

You too muchee laugh ! What for sing.
I tink so you no savvy t'hat ling !
Supposey you no blong clever inside
More betta *you* go walk top-side,
   Top-side galow !

Bayard Taylor (1825–1878)

THE LAY OF MACARONI
(*Swinburne*)

A S a wave that steals when the winds are stormy
 From creek to cave of the curving shore,
Buffeted, blown, and broken before me,
 Scattered and spread to its sunlit core :

As a dove that dips in the dark of maples
　　To sip the sweetness of shelter and shade,
I kneel in thy nimbus, O noon of Naples,
　　I bathe in thy beauty, by thee embayed.

What is it ails me that I should sing of her?
　　The queen of the flashes and flames that were!
Yea, I have felt the shuddering sting of her,
　　The flower-sweet throat and the hands of her!
I have swayed and sung to the sound of her psalters,
　　I have danced her dances of dizzy delight,
I have hallowed mine hair to the horns of her altars
　　Between the nightingale's song and the night!

What is it, Queen, that now I should do for thee?
　　What is it now I should ask at thine hands?
Blow of the trumpets thine children once blew for
　　　thee?
　　Break from thine feet and thine bosom the bands?
Nay, as sweet as the songs of Leone Leoni,
　　And gay as her garments of gem-sprinkled gold,
She gives me mellifluous, mild macaroni,
　　The choice of her children when cheeses are old!

And over we hover, as if by the wings of it,
　　Frayed in the furnace by flame that is fleet,
The curious coils and the strenuous strings of it,
　　Dropping, diminishing down as I sat;
Lo! and the beautiful Queen, as she brings of it,
　　Lifts me the links of the limitless chain,
Bidding mine mouth chant the splendidest things
　　　of it,
　　Out of the wealth of my wonderful brain!

Behold ! I have done it : my stomach is smitten
  With sweets of the surfeit her hands have unrolled.
Italia, mine cheeks with thine kisses are bitten :
  I am broken with beauty, stabbed, slaughtered,
      and sold !
No man of thy millions is more macaronied,
  Save mighty Mazzini, than musical Me :
The souls of the Ages shall stand as astonied,
  And faint in the flame I am fanning for thee !

CIMABUELLA

(*D. G. Rossetti*)

FAIR-TINTED cheeks, clear eyelids drawn,
    In crescent curves above the light
Of eyes, whose dim, uncertain dawn
    Becomes not day : a forehead white
Beneath long yellow heaps of hair :
She is so strange she must be fair.

Had she sharp, slant-wise wings outspread,
    She were an angel ; but she stands
With flat dead gold behind her head,
    And lilies in her long thin hands :
Her folded mantle, gathered in,
Falls to her feet as it were tin.

Her nose is keen as pointed flame ;
    Her crimson lips no thing express ;
And never dread of saintly blame
    Held down her heavy eyelashes :
To guess what she were thinking of,
Precludeth any meaner love.

An azure carpet, fringed with gold,
  Sprinkled with scarlet spots, I laid
Before her straight, cool feet unrolled :
  But she nor sound nor movement made
(Albeit I heard a soft, shy smile,
  Printing her neck a moment's while) ;

And I was shamed through all my mind
  For that she spake not, neither kissed,
But stared right past me. Lo ! behind
  Me stood, in pink and amethyst,
Sword-girt and velvet-doubleted,
A tall, gaunt youth, with frowzy head,

Wide nostrils in the air, dull eyes,
  Thick lips that simpered, but, ah me !
I saw, with most forlorn surprise,
  He was the Thirteenth Century !
I but the Nineteenth : then despair
Curdled beneath my curling hair.

O, Love and Fate ! How could she choose
  My rounded outlines, broader brain,
And my resuscitated Muse ?
  Some tears she shed, but whether pain
Or joy in him unlocked their source,
I could not fathom which, of course.

But I from missals, quaintly bound,
  With cither and with clavichord
Will sing her songs of sovran sound :
  Belike her pity will afford
Such faint return as suits a saint
So sweetly done in verse and paint.

THE PROMISSORY NOTE
(*E. A. Poe*)

IN the lonesome latter years,
   (Fatal years !)
To the dropping of my tears
Danced the mad and mystic spheres
In a rounded, reeling rune,
    'Neath the moon,
To the dripping and the dropping of my tears.

Ah my soul is swathed in gloom,
   (Ulalume !)
In a dim Titanic tomb,
For my gaunt and gloomy soul
Ponders o'er the penal scroll
O'er the parchment (not a rhyme),
Out of place—out of time,—
I am shredded, shorn, unshifty,
   (O, the fifty !)
And the days have passed, the three,
   Over me !
And the debit and the credit are as one to him and
   me !

'Twas the random runes I wrote
At the bottom of the note
   (Wrote and freely,
   Gave to Greeley),
In the middle of the night
On the yellow, moonless night,
When the stars were out of sight,
When my pulses, like a knell,
   (Israfel !)

Danced with dim and dying fays
O'er the ruins of my days,
O'er the dimeless, timeless days,
When the fifty, drawn at thirty,
Seeming thrifty, yet the dirty
Lucre of the market, was the most that I could
    raise!
      Fiends controlled it,
      (Let him hold it!)
Devils held for me the inkstand and the pen;
Now the days of grace are o'er,
      (Ah, Lenore!)
I am but as other men;
What is time, time, time,
To my rare and runic rhyme,
To my random, reeling rhyme,
By the sands along the shore,
Where the tempest whispers, "Pay him!" and I
    answer "Never more!"

FROM "THE TAMING OF THEMISTOCLES"
(*William Morris*)

"HE must be holpen; yet how help shall I,
    Steeped to the lips in ancient misery,
And by the newer grief apparelléd?
If that I throw these ashes on mine head,
Do this thing for thee,—while about my way
A shadow gathers, and the piteous day,
So wan and bleak for very loneliness,
Turneth from sight of such untruthfulness?"
Therewith he caught an arrow from the sheaf,
And brake the shaft in witlessness of grief;

But Chiton's vest, such dismal fear she had,
Shook from the heart that sorely was a-drad,
And she began, withouten any pause,
To say : " Why break the old Aetolian laws ?
Send this man forth, that never harm hath done,
Between the risen and the setten sun."

And next, they wandered to a steepy hill
Whence all the land was lying grey and still,
And not a living creature there might be
From the cold mountains to the salt, cold sea ;
Only, within a little cove, one sail
Shook, as it whimpered at the cruel gale,
And the mast moaned from chafing of the rope ;
So all was pain : they saw not any hope.

THE BALLAD OF HIRAM HOVER
(*Whittier*)

WHERE the Moosatockmaguntic
    Pours its waters in the Skuntic,
  Met, along the forest-side,
  Hiram Hover, Huldah Hyde.

She, a maiden fair and dapper ;
He, a red-haired, stalwart trapper,
  Hunting beaver, mink, and skunk,
  In the woodlands of Squeedunk.

She, Pentucket's pensive daughter,
Walked beside the Skuntic water,
  Gathering, in her apron wet,
  Snakeroot, mint, and bouncing-bet.

"Why," he murmured, loath to leave her,
"Gather yarbs for chills and fever,
    When a lovyer, bold and true,
    Only waits to gather you?"

"Go," she answered, "I'm not hasty;
I prefer a man more tasty:
    Leastways, one to please me well
    Should not have a beasty smell."

"Haughty Huldah!" Hiram answered;
"Mind and heart alike are cancered:
    Jest look here! these peltries give
    Cash, wherefrom a pair may live.

"I, you think am but a vagrant,
Trapping beasts by no means fragrant:
    Yet—I'm sure it's worth a thank—
    I've a handsome sum in bank."

Turned and vanished Hiram Hover;
And, before the year was over
    Huldah, with the yarbs she sold,
    Bought a cape, against the cold.

Black and thick the furry cape was;
Of a stylish cut the shape was,
    And the girls, in all the town,
    Envied Huldah up and down.

Then, at last, one winter morning,
Hiram came, without a warning:
    "Either," said he, "you are blind,
    Huldah, or you've changed your mind.

" Me you snub for trapping varmints,
Yet you take the skins for garments :
   Since you wear the skunk and mink,
   There's no harm in me, I think."

" Well," she said, " we will not quarrel,
Hiram ; I accept the moral,
   Now the fashion's so, I guess
   I can't hardly do no less."

Thus the trouble all was over
Of the love of Hiram Hover ;
   Thus he made sweet Huldah Hyde
   Huldah Hover as his bride.

Love employs, with equal favour
Things of good and evil savour ;
   That, which first appeared to part,
   Warmed, at last, the maiden's heart.

Under one impartial banner,
Life, the hunter, Love the tanner,
   Draw, from every beast they snare,
   Comfort for a wedded pair !

Edward Bradley ("Cuthbert Bede") (1827–1889)

IN IMMEMORIAM
(*Tennyson*)

WE seek to know, and, knowing, seek ;
   We seek, we know, and every sense
Is trembling with the great intense,
And vibrating to what we speak.

We ask too much, we seek too oft;
  We know enough, and should no more;
  And yet we skim through Fancy's lore,
And look to earth, and not aloft.

A something comes from out the gloom—
  I know it not, nor seek to know—
  I only see it swell and grow,
And more than this would not presume.

Meseems, a circling void I fill,
  And I unchanged where all is change
  It seems unreal—I own it strange—
Yet nurse the thoughts I cannot kill.

I hear the ocean's surging tide
  Raise, quiring on, its carol-tune;
  I watch the golden-sickled moon,
And clearer voices call beside.

O sea! whose ancient ripples lie
  On red-ribbed sands where seaweeds shone;
  O moon! whose golden sickle's gone,
O voices all! like you, I die!   (*Dies.*)

Mortimer Collins (1827–1876)

SALAD
(*Swinburne*)

O COOL in the summer is salad,
    And warm in the winter is love;
And a poet shall sing you a ballad
    Delicious thereon and thereof.

A singer am I, if no sinner,
  My muse has a marvellous wing,
And I willingly worship at Dinner
    The Sirens of Spring.

Take endive—like love it is bitter,
  Take beet—for like love it is red :
Crisp leaf of the lettuce shall glitter,
  And cress from the rivulet's bed :
Anchovies, foam-born, like the lady
  Whose beauty has maddened this bard ;
And olives, from groves that are shady,
  And eggs—boil 'em hard.

Dante Gabriel Rossetti (1828–1882)

MAC CRACKEN
(*Tennyson*)

GETTING his pictures, like his supper, cheap,
  Far Far away in Belfast by the Sea,
His watchful, one-eyed, uninvaded sleep
Mac Cracken sleepeth. While the P.R.B.
Must keep the shady side, he walks a swell
Through spungings of perennial growth and height
And far away, in Belfast out of sight,
By many an open " do " and secret sell
Fresh daubers he makes swift to scarify,
And fleece with pliant shears the slumbering
    " green."
There he has lied, though aged, and will lie
Fattening on ill-got pictures in his sleep,
Till some Pre-Raphaelite prove for him too deep.
Then once by Hunt and Ruskin to be seen,
Insolvent he will turn, and in the Queen's Bench die.

Charles Stuart Calverley (1831–1884)
THE COCK AND THE BULL
(*Browning*)

YOU see this pebble-stone ? It's a thing I
    bought
Of a bit of a chit of a boy i' the mid o' the day—
I like to dock the smaller parts-o'-speech,
As we curtail the already cur-tail'd cur
(You catch the paronomasia, play 'po' words ?)
Did, rather, i' the pre-Landseerian days.
Well, to my muttons. I purchased the concern,
And clapt it i' my poke, having given for same
By way o' chop, swop, barter or exchange—
" Chop " was my snickering dandiprat's own term—
One shilling and fourpence, current coin o' the realm.
O-n-e one and f-o-u-r four
Pence, one and fourpence—you are with me, sir ?—
What hour it skills not : ten or eleven o' the clock,
One day (and what a roaring day it was
Go shop or sight-see—bar a spit o' rain !)
In February, eighteen sixty-nine,
Alexandrina Victoria, Fidei
Hm—hm—how runs the jargon ? being on throne.

Such, sir, are all the facts, succinctly put,
The basis or substratum—what you will—
Of the impending eighty thousand lines.
" Not much in 'em either," quoth perhaps simple
    Hodge.
But there's a superstructure. Wait a bit.
Mark first the rationale of the thing :
Hear logic rivel and levigate the deed.

That shilling—and for matter o' that, the pence—
I had o' course upo' me—wi' me say—
(*Mecum*'s the Latin, make a note o' that)
When I popp'd pen i' stand, scratch'd ear, wiped snout,
(Let everybody wipe his own himself)
Sniff'd—tch !—at snuffbox ; tumbled up, he-heed,
Haw-haw'd (not hee-haw'd, that's another guess
     thing :)
Then fumbled at, and stumbled out of, door,
I shoved the timber ope wi' my omoplat ;
And *in vestibulo*, i' the lobby to wit,
(Iacobi Facciolati's rendering, sir,)
Donn'd galligaskins, antigropeloes,
And so forth ; and, complete with hat and gloves,
One on and one a-dangle i' my hand,
And ombrifuge (Lord love you !) case o' rain,
I flopp'd forth, 'sbuddikins ! on my own ten toes,
(I do assure you there be ten of them),
And went clump-clumping up hill and down dale
To find myself o' the sudden i' front o' the boy.
Put case I hadn't 'em on me, could I ha' bought
This sort-o' kind-o'-what-you-might-call toy,
This pebble-thing, o' the boy-thing ? Q.E.D.
That's proven without aid from mumping Pope,
Sleep porporate or bloated Cardinal.
(Isn't it, old Fatchaps ? You're in Euclid, now.)
So, having the shilling—having i' fact a lot—
And pence and halfpence, ever so many o' them,
I purchased, as I think I said before,
The pebble (lapis, lapidis, -di, -dem, -de—
What nouns 'crease short i' the genitive, Fatchaps,
     eh ?)
O' the boy, a bare-legg'd beggarly son of a gun,
For one-and-fourpence. Here we are again.

Now Law steps in, bigwigg'd, voluminous-jaw'd
Investigates and re-investigates.
Was the transaction illegal? Law shakes head.
Perpend, sir, all the bearings of the case.

At first the coin was mine, the chattel his.
But now (by virtue of the said exchange
And barter) *vice versa* all the coin,
Per juris operationem, vests
I' the boy and his assigns till ding o' doom;
In *sœculo sœculo-o-o-orum*;
(I think I hear the Abate mouth out that.)
To have and hold the same to him and then . . .
Confer some idiot on Conveyancing.
Whereas the pebble and every part thereof,
And all that appertaineth thereunto,
Quodcunque pertinet ad eam rem,
(I fancy, sir, my Latin's rather pat)
Or shall, will, may, might, can, could, would or
        should,
(*Subandi cœtera*—clap me to the close——
For what's the good of law in a case o' the kind?)
Is mine to all intents and purposes.
This settled, I resume the thread o' the tale.

Now for a touch o' the vendor's quality.
He says a gen'lman bought a pebble of him,
(This pebble i' sooth, sir, which I hold i' my hand)—
And paid for't *like* a gen'lman, on the nail.
" Did I o'ercharge him a ha'penny? Devil a bit.
Fiddlepin's end! Get out, you blazing ass!
Gabble o' the goose. Don't bugaboo-baby *me*!
Go double or quits? Ya! tittup! what's the odds?"
—There's the transaction view'd i' the vendor's light.

Next ask that dumpled hag, stood snuffling by,
With her three frowsy blowsy brats o' babes,
The scum o' the kennel, cream o' the filth-heap—
    Faugh !
Aie, aie, aie, aie ! ὀτοτοτοτοτοτ
('Stead which we blurt out Hoighty toighty now)—
And the baker and the candlestickmaker, and Jack
    and Jill,
Blear'd Goody this and queasy Gaffer that.
Ask the schoolmaster. Take schoolmaster first.

He saw a gentleman purchase from a lad
A stone, and pay for it *rite*, on the square,
And carry it off *per saltum*, jauntily,
Propria quae maribus, gentleman's property now
(Agreeably to the law explain'd above),
In proprium usum, for his private ends.
The boy he chuck'd a brown i' the air, and bit
I' the face the shilling : heaved a thumping stone
At a lean hen that ran cluck clucking by,
(And hit her, dead as nail i' post o' door,)
Then abiit—what's the Ciceronian phrase ?—
Excessit, evasit, erupit—off slogs boy ;
Off like bird, *avi similis*—(you observed
The dative ? Pretty i' the Mantuan !)—*Anglice*,
Off in three flea skips. *Hactenus*, so far,
So good, *tam bene*. *Bene, satis, male*—,
Where was I with my trope 'bout one in a quag ?
I did once hitch the syntax into verse :
Verbum personale, a verb personal,
Concordat—ay, " agrees ", old Fatchaps—*cum
Nominativo*, with its nominative,
Genere, i' point o' gender, *numero*,
O' number, *et persona*, and person. *Ut*,

Instance : *Sol ruit*, down flops sun, *et* and
Montes umbrantur, out flounce mountains.   Pah !
Excuse me, sir, I think I'm going mad.
You see the trick on 't though, and can yourself
Continue the discourse *ad libitum.*
It takes up about eighty thousand lines,
A thing imagination boggles at :
And might, odds-bobs, sir ! in judicious hands,
Extend from here to Mesopotamy.

BEER

(*Byron*)

IN those old days which poets say were golden—
　　(Perhaps they laid the gilding on themselves :
And, if they did, I'm all the more beholden
　　To those brown dwellers in my dusty shelves,
Who talk to me "in language quaint and olden "
　　Of gods and demigods and fauns and elves,
Pan with his pipes, and Bacchus with his leopards,
And staid young goddesses who flirt with shep-
　　　　herds :)

In those old days, the Nymph called Etiquette
　　(Appalling thought to dwell on) was not born.
They had their May, but no Mayfair as yet,
　　No fashions varying as the hues of morn.
Just as they pleased they dressed and drank and
　　　　ate,
　　Sang hymns to Ceres (their John Barleycorn)
And danced unchaperoned, and laughed unchecked,
And were no doubt extremely incorrect.

Yet do I think their theory was pleasant :
   And oft, I own, my " wayward fancy roams "
Back to those times, so different from the present ;
   When no one smoked cigars, nor gave At-homes,
Nor smote a billiard-ball, nor winged a pheasant,
   Nor " did " their hair by means of long-tailed
      combs,
Nor migrated to Brighton once a year,
Nor—most astonishing of all—drank Beer.

No, they did not drink Beer, " which brings me to "
(As Gilpin said) " the middle of my song."
Not that " the middle " is precisely true,
   Or else I should not tax your patience long :
If I had said " beginning " it might do ;
   But I have a dislike to quoting wrong :
I was unlucky—sinned against, not sinning—
When Cowper wrote down " middle " for " begin-
      ning."

So to proceed.   That abstinence from Malt
   Has always struck me as extremely curious.
The Greek mind must have had some vital fault,
   That they should stick to liquors so injurious—
(Wine, water, tempered p'raps with Attic salt)—
   And not at once invent that mild, luxurious,
And artful beverage, Beer.   How the digestion
Got on without it, is a startling question.

Had they digestions ? and an actual body
   Such as dyspepsia might make attacks on ?
Were they abstract ideas—(like Tom Noddy
   And Mr. Briggs)—or men, like Jones and Jackson ?

Then Nectar—was that beer, or whisky-toddy ?
  Some say the Gaelic mixture, *I* the Saxon :
I think a strict adherence to the latter
Might make some Scots less pigheaded, and fatter.

Besides, Bon Gaultier definitely shows
  That the real beverage for feasting gods on
Is a soft compound, grateful to the nose
  And also to the palate, known as " Hodgson."
I know a man—a tailor's son—who rose
  To be a peer : and this I would lay odds on,
(Though in his Memoirs it may not appear,)
That that man owed his rise to copious Beer.

O Beer ! O Hodgson, Guinness, Allsopp, Bass !
  Names that should be on every infant's tongue !
Shall days and months and years and centuries
      pass,
  And still your merits be unrecked, unsung ?
Oh ! I have gazed into my foaming glass,
  And wished that lyre could yet again be strung
Which once rang prophet-like through Greece, and
      taught her
Misguided sons that " the best drink was water."

How would he now recant that wild opinion,
  And sing—as would that I could sing—of you !
I was not born (alas !) the " Muses' minion ",
  I'm not poetical, not even blue :
And he (we know) but strives with waxen pinion
  Whoe'er he is that entertains the view
Of emulating Pindar, and will be
Sponsor at last to some now nameless sea.

Oh ! when the green slopes of Arcadia burned
  With all the lustre of the dying day,
And on Cithaeron's brow the reaper turned,
  (Humming, of course, in his delightful way,
How Lycidas was dead, and how concerned
  The Nymphs were when they saw his lifeless clay ;
And how rock told to rock the dreadful story
That poor young Lycidas was gone to glory :)

What would that lone and labouring soul have
    given,
  At that soft moment, for a pewter pot !
How had the mists that dimmed his eye been riven,
  And Lycidas and sorrow all forgot !
If his own grandmother had died unshriven,
  In two short seconds he'd have recked it not ;
Such power hath Beer.   The heart which Grief hath
    canker'd
Hath one unfailing remedy—the Tankard.

Coffee is good, and so no doubt is cocoa ;
  Tea did for Johnson and the Chinamen :
When " Dulce est desipere in loco "
  Was written, real Falernian winged the pen.
When a rapt audience has encored " Fra Poco "
  Or " Casta Diva ", I have heard that then
The Prima Donna, smiling herself out,
Recruits her flagging powers with bottled stout.

But what is coffee, but a noxious berry,
  Born to keep used-up Londoners awake ?
What is Falernian, what is Port or Sherry,
  But vile concoctions to make dull heads ache ?

Nay stout itself (though good with oysters, very)—
  Is not a thing your reading man should take.
He that would shine, and petrify his tutor,
Should drink draught Allsopp in its " native pew-
    ter."

But hark ! a sound is stealing on my ear—
  A soft and silvery sound—I know it well.
Its tinkling tells me that a time is near
  Precious to me—it is the Dinner Bell.
O blessed Bell ! Thou bringest beef and beer,
  Thou bringest good things more than tongue may
    tell :
Seared is (of course) my heart—but unsubdued
Is, and shall be, my appetite for food.

I go. Untaught and feeble is my pen :
  But on one statement I may safely venture :
That few of our most highly gifted men
  Have more appreciation of the trencher.
I go. One pound of British beef, and then
  What Mr. Swiveller called " a modest quencher " ;
That, home-returning, I may " soothly say ",
" Fate cannot touch me : I have dined to-day."

THE AULD WIFE : BALLAD

(Jean Ingelow)

THE auld wife sat at her ivied door,
    (Butter and eggs and a pound of cheese)
A thing she had frequently done before ;
  And her spectacles lay on her aproned knees.

The piper he piped on the hill-top high,
  (*Butter and eggs and a pound of cheese*)
Till the cow said " I die," and the goose asked
    " Why ? "
  And the dog said nothing, but searched for fleas.

The farmer he strove through the square farmyard ;
  (*Butter and eggs and a pound of cheese*)
His last brew of ale was a trifle hard—
  The connexion of which with the plot one sees.

The farmer's daughter hath frank blue eyes ;
  (*Butter and eggs and a pound of cheese*)
She hears the rooks caw in the windy skies,
  As she sits at her lattice and shells her peas.

The farmer's daughter hath ripe red lips ;
  (*Butter and eggs and a pound of cheese*)
If you try to approach her, away she skips
  Over tables and chairs with apparent ease.

The farmer's daughter hath soft brown hair ;
  (*Butter and eggs and a pound of cheese*)
And I met with a ballad, I can't say where,
  Which wholly consisted of lines like these.

Part II

She sat, with her hands 'neath her dimpled cheeks,
  (*Butter and eggs and a pound of cheese*)
And spake not a word. While a lady speaks
  There is hope, but she didn't even sneeze.

A.P.   H

She sat, with her hands 'neath her crimson cheeks,
    (*Butter and eggs and a pound of cheese*)
She gave up mending her father's breeks,
    And let the cat roll in her new chemise.

She sat, with her hands 'neath her burning cheeks,
    (*Butter and eggs and a pound of cheese*)
And gazed at the piper for thirteen weeks;
    Then she followed him out o'er the misty leas.

Her sheep followed her, as their tails did them.
    (*Butter and eggs and a pound of cheese*)
And this song is considered a perfect gem,
    And as to the meaning, it's what you please.

LOVERS, AND A REFLECTION

IN moss prankt dells which the sunbeams flatter
    (And heaven it knoweth what that may mean;
Meaning, however, is no great matter)
    Where woods are a-tremble, with rifts atween;

Through God's own heather we wonned together,
    I and my Willie (O love, my love):
I need hardly remark it was glorious weather,
    And flitterbats wavered alow, above:

Boats were curtseying, rising, bowing,
    (Boats in that climate are so polite),
And sands were a ribbon of green endowing
    And O, the sundazzle on bark and bight!

Through the rare red heather we danced together,
  (O love, my Willie!) and smelt for flowers:
I must mention again it was glorious weather,
  Rhymes are so scarce in this world of ours:—

By rises that flushed with their purple favours,
  Through becks that brattled o'er grasses sheen,
We walked and waded, we two young shavers,
  Thanking our stars we were both so green.

We journeyed in parallels, I and Willie,
  In fortunate parallels! Butterflies,
Hid in weltering shadows of daffodilly
  Or marjoram, kept making peacock eyes:

Song-birds darted about, some inky
  As coal, some snowy (I ween) as curds;
Or rosy as pinks, or as roses pinky—
  They reck of no eerie To-come, those birds!

But they skim over bents which the mill stream
    washes,
  Or hang in the lift 'neath a white cloud's
    hem;
They need no parasols, no goloshes;
  And good Mrs. Trimmer she feedeth them.

Then we thrid God's cowslips (as erst his heather)
  That endowed the wan grass with their golden
    blooms
And snapped—(it was perfectly charming weather)
  Our fingers at Fate and her goddess-glooms:

And Willie 'gan sing (O, his notes were fluty ;
   Wafts fluttered them out to the white-winged
     sea)—
Something made up of rhymes that have done much
     duty
   Rhymes (better to put it) of " ancientry " :

Bowers of flowers encountered showers
   In William's carol—(O love, my Willie !)
Then he bade sorrow borrow from blithe to-morrow
   I quite forget what—say a daffodilly :

A nest in a hollow, " with buds to follow,"
   I think occurred next in his nimble strain ;
And clay that was " kneaden " of course in Eden—
   A rhyme most novel, I do maintain :

Mists, bones, the singer himself, love-stories,
   And all least furlable things got " furled " ;
Not with any designs to conceal their glories
   But simply and solely to rhyme with " world."

.   .   .   .

O, if billows and pillows and hours and flowers,
   And all the brave rhymes of an elder day,
Could be furled together this genial weather,
   And carted or carried on " wafts " away,
Nor ever again trotted out—ah me !
How much fewer volumes of verse there'd be !

PROVERBIAL PHILOSOPHY

(*Martin Tupper*)

INTRODUCTORY

ART thou beautiful, oh my daughter, as the budding rose of April?

Are all thy motions music, and is poetry throned in thine eye?

Then hearken unto me; and I will make the bud a fair flower;

I will plant it upon the bank of Elegance, and water it with the water of Cologne;

And in the season it shall "come out," yea bloom, the pride of the parterre;

Ladies shall marvel at its beauty, and a Lord shall pluck it at the last.

OF PROPRIETY

Study first Propriety: for she is indeed the Polestar

Which shall guide the artless maiden through the mazes of Vanity Fair;

Nay, she is the golden chain which holdeth together Society;

The lamp by whose light young Psyche shall approach unblamed her Eros.

Verily Truth is as Eve, which was ashamed being naked;

Wherefore doth Propriety dress her with the fair foliage of artifice:

And when she is drest, behold! she knoweth not herself again.—

I walked in the Forest ; and above me stood the
    Yew,

Stood like a slumbering giant, shrouded in impene-
    trable shade ;

Then I past into the citizen's garden, and marked a
    tree clipt into shape

(The giant's locks had been shorn by the Delilah-
    shears of Decorum ;)

And I said, " Surely nature is goodly ; but how
    much goodlier is Art ! "

I heard the wild notes of the lark floating far over
    the blue sky,

And my foolish heart went after him, and lo ! I
    blessed him as he rose ;

Foolish ! for far better is the trained boudoir bull-
    finch,

Which pipeth the semblance of a tune, and mechan-
    ically draweth up water :

And the reinless steed of the desert, though his neck
    be clothed with thunder,

Must yield to him that danceth and " moveth in the
    circles " at Astley's.

For verily, oh my daughter, the world is a mas-
    querade,

And God made thee one thing, that thou mightest
    make thyself another :

A maiden's heart is as champagne, ever aspiring
    and struggling upwards,

And it needeth that its motions be checked by the
    silver cork of Propriety :

He that can afford the price, his be the precious
    treasure,

Let him drink deeply of its sweetness, nor grumble
    if it tasteth of the cork.

Of Friendship

Choose judiciously thy friends ; for to discard them
    is undesirable,

Yet it is better to drop thy friends, oh my daughter,
    than to drop thy " H's."

Dost thou know a wise woman ? yea, wiser than the
    children of light ?

Hath she a position ? and a title ? and are her par-
    ties in the Morning Post ?

If thou dost, cleave unto her, and give up unto her
    thy body and mind ;

Think with her ideas, and distribute thy smiles at
    her bidding :

So shalt thou become like unto her ; and thy man-
    ners shall be " formed ",

And thy name shall be a Sesame at which the doors
    of the great shall fly open :

Thou shalt know every Peer, his arms, and the date
    of his creation,

His pedigree and their intermarriages, and cousins
    to the sixth remove :

Thou shalt kiss the hand of Royalty, and lo ! in
    next morning's papers,

Side by side with rumours of wars, and accounts of
    shipwrecks and sieges,

Shall appear thy name, and the minutiæ of thy
    head-dress and petticoat,

For an enraptured public to muse upon over their
    matutinal muffin.

Walter William Skeat (1831–1912)

A CLERK THER WAS OF CAUNTEBRIGGE ALSO

(*Chaucer*)

A CLERK ther was of Cauntebrigge also,
    That unto rowing haddè long y-go.
Of thinnè shidès wolde he shippès makè,
And he was nat right fat, I undertake.
And whan his ship he wrought had attè fullè,
Right gladly by the river wolde he pullè,
And eek returne as blythly as he wentè.
Him rekkèd nevere that the sonne him brentè,
Ne stinted he his cours for reyn ne snowè ;
It was a joyè for to seen him rowè !
Yit was him lever, in his shelves newè,
Six oldè textès, clad in greenish hewè,
Of Chaucer and his olde poesyè
Than ale, or wyn of Lepe, or Malvoisyè.
And therwithal he wex a philosofre ;
And peyned him to gadren gold in cofre
Of sundry folk ; and al that he mighte hentè
On textès and emprinting he it spentè ;
And busily gan bokès to purveyè
For hem that yeve him wherwith to scoleyè.
Of glossaryès took he hede and curè ;
And when he spyèd had, by aventurè,
A word that semèd him or strange or rarè,
To henten it anon he noldè sparè,
But wolde it on a shrede of paper wrytè,
And in a cheste he dide his shredes whytè,
And preyèd every man to doon the samè ;
Swich maner study was to him but gamè.

And on this wysè many a yeer he wroughtè,
Ay storing every shreed that men him broughtè,
Til, attè lastè, from the noble pressè
Of Clarendoun, at Oxenforde, I gessè,
Cam stalking forth the Grete Dictionarie
That no man wel may pinche at ne contrarie.
But for to tellen alle his queinte geres,
They wolden occupye wel seven yeres ;
Therefore I passe as lightly as I may ;
Ne speke I of his hatte or his array,
Ne how his berd by every wind was shake
When as, for hete, his hat he wolde of take.
Souning in Erly English was his speche,
" And gladly wolde he lerne, and gladly teche."

Lewis Carroll (1833–1898)
FATHER WILLIAM
(*Southey*)

" YOU are old, Father William," the young man
      said,
   " And your hair has become very white ;
And yet you incessantly stand on your head,
   Do you think at your age it is right ? "

' In my youth," Father William replied to his son,
   " I feared it might injure the brain,
But now that I'm perfectly sure I have none,
   Why, I do it again and again."

" You are old," said the youth, " as I mentioned
      before,
   And have grown most uncommonly fat ;
Yet you turned a back somersault in at the door,
   Pray, *what* is the reason of that ? "

" In my youth," said the sage, as he shook his grey
      locks,
  " I kept all my limbs very supple,
By the use of this ointment—one shilling the box,
  Allow me to sell you a couple."

" You are old," said the youth, " and your jaws are
      too weak
  For anything tougher than suet,
Yet you finished the goose, with the bones and the
      beak,
  Pray, how did you manage to do it ? "

" In my youth," said his father, " I took to the
      law,
  And argued each case with my wife,
And the muscular strength which it gave to my
      jaw
  Has lasted the rest of my life."

" You are old," said the youth, " one would hardly suppose
  That your eye was as steady as ever ;
Yet you balance an eel on the end of your nose,—
  What made you so *awfully* clever ? "

" I have answered three questions and that is
      enough,"
  Said his father ; " don't give yourself airs.
Do you think I can listen all day to such stuff ?
  Be off, or I'll kick you downstairs ! "

THE VOICE OF THE LOBSTER
(*Watts*)

" 'TIS the voice of the Lobster : I heard him
         declare
' You have baked me too brown, I must sugar my
     hair.'
As a duck with its eyelids, so he with his nose
Trims his belt and his buttons, and turns out his
     toes.
When the sands are all dry, he is gay as a lark,
And will talk in contemptuous tones of the
     Shark :
But, when the tide rises and sharks are around;
His voice has a timid and tremulous sound.

" I passed by his garden, and marked, with one eye
How the Owl and the Panther were sharing a pie ,
The Panther took pie-crust, and gravy, and meat,
While the Owl had the dish as its share of the
     treat.
When the pie was all finished, the Owl, as a boon,
Was kindly permitted to pocket the spoon ;
While the Panther received knife and fork with a
     growl,
And concluded the banquet by——"

TURTLE SOUP
(*Ann Taylor*)

BEAUTIFUL Soup, so rich and green,
         Waiting in a hot tureen !
Who for such dainties would not stoop ?

Soup of the evening, beautiful Soup ?
Soup of the evening, beautiful Soup ?
   Beau-ootiful Soo-oop !
   Beau-ootiful Soo-oop !
Soo-oop of the e-e-evening,
   Beautiful, beautiful Soup !

Beautiful Soup !   Who cares for fish,
Game, or any other dish ?
Who would not give all else for two-p
ennyworth only of beautiful Soup ?
Pennyworth only of beautiful Soup ?
   Beau-ootiful Soo-oop !
   Beau-ootiful Soo-oop !
Soo-oop of the e-e-evening,
   Beautiful, beauti-FUL SOUP !

Thomas Hood, the Younger (1835–1874)

POETS AND LINNETS
(*Robert Browning*)

WHERE'ER there's a thistle to feed a linnet
   And linnets are plenty, thistles rife—
Or an acorn cup to catch dew-drops in it,
There's ample promise of further life.
Now, mark how we begin it.

For linnets will follow, if linnets are minded,
   As blows the white feather parachute ;
And ships will reel by the tempest blinded—
By, ships, and shiploads of men to boot !
How deep whole fleets you'll find hid.

And we'll blow the thistle-down hither and thither,
Forgetful of linnets and men, and God.
The dew! for its want an oak will wither—
By the dull hoof into the dust is trod,
And then who strikes the cithar?

But thistles were only for donkeys intended,
And that donkeys are common enough is clear.
And that drop! what a vessel it might have be-
    friended,
Does it add any flavour to Glugabib's beer?
Well, there's my musing ended.

A CATCH
(*Swinburne*)

IF you were queen of bloaters,
    And I were king of soles,
The sea we'd wag our fins in,
Nor heed the crooked pins in
The water dropt by boaters,
    To catch our heedless joles;
If you were queen of bloaters—
    And I were king of soles.

If you were LADY MILE-END,
    And I were DUKE OF BOW,
We'd marry and we'd quarrel,
And then, to point the moral
Should LORD PENZANCE his file lend,
    Our chains to overthrow;
If you were LADY MILE-END,
    And I were DUKE OF BOW.

If you were chill November,
　　And I were sunny June,
I'd not with love pursue you ;
For I should be to woo you
(You're foggy, pray remember)
　　A most egregious spoon ;
If you were chill November,
　　And I were sunny June.

If you were cook to Venus,
　　And I were J 19,
When missus was out dining,
　　Our suppetites combining,
We'd oft contrive between us .
　　To keep the platter clean ;
If you were cook to Venus,
　　And I were J 19.

If you were but a jingle,
　　And I were but a rhyme,
We'd keep this up for ever,
Nor think it very clever,
A grain of sense to mingle
　　At times with simple chime ;
If you were but a jingle,
　　And I were but a rhyme.

W. S. Gilbert (1836–1911)

THE BOLD MOUNSEER

I SHIPPED, d'ye see, in a Revenue sloop,
　　And, off Cape Finisterre,
　　　A merchantman we see,
　　　A Frenchman going free,

So we made for the bold Mounseer,
           D'ye see ?
We made for the bold Mounseer.
But she proved to be a frigate—and she up with her
    ports,
    And fires with a thirty-two !
        It come uncommon near,
        But we answered with a cheer,
    Which paralysed the Parly-voo,
           D'ye see ?
    Which paralysed the Parly-voo !

Then our Captain he up and he says, says he,
    " That chap we need not fear,—
        We can take her if we like,
        She is sartin for to strike,
    For she's only a darned Mounseer,
           D'ye see ?
    She's only a darned Mounseer,
But to fight a French fal-lal—it's like hittin' of a
    gal—
    It's a lubberly thing for to do ;
        For we, with all our faults,
        Why, we're sturdy British salts,
    While she's only a Parley-voo,
           D'ye see ?
    A miserable Parley-voo ! "

So we up with our helm, and we scuds before the
    breeze
    As we gives a compassionating cheer ;
        Froggee answers with a shout
        As he sees us go about,

Which was grateful of the poor Mounseer !
    D'ye see ?
Which was grateful of the poor Mounseer !
And I'll wager in their joy they kissed each other's
    cheek
(Which is what them furriners do),
    And they blessed their lucky stars
    We were hardy British tars
Who had pity on a poor Parley-voo,
    D'ye see ?
Who had pity on a poor Parley-voo !

Algernon Charles Swinburne (1837–1909)

NEPHELIDIA

(*A. C. Swinburne*)

FROM the depth of the dreamy decline of the
    dawn through a notable nimbus of nebulous
    moon-shine,
  Pallid and pink as the palm of the flag-flower that
    flickers with fear of the flies as they float,
Are they looks of our lovers that lustrously lean
    from a marvel of mystic miraculous moon-
    shine,
  These that we feel in the blood of our blushes
    that thicken and threaten with throbs through
    the throat ?
Thicken and thrill as a theatre thronged at appeal
    of an actor's appalled agitation,
  Fainter with fear of the fires of the future than
    pale with the promise of pride in the past ;

Flushed with the famishing fullness of fever that
    reddens with radiance of rathe recreation,
  Gaunt as the ghastliest of glimpses that gleam
    through the gloom of the gloaming when ghosts
    go aghast ?
Nay, for the nick of the tick of the time is a tremu-
    lous touch on the temples of terror,
  Strained as the sinews yet strenuous with strife
    of the dead who is dumb as the dust-heaps of
    death :
Surely no soul is it, sweet as the spasm of erotic
    emotional exquisite error,
  Bathed in the balms of beatified bliss, beatific
    itself by beatitude's breath.
Surely no spirit or sense of a soul that was soft to
    the spirit and soul of our senses
  Sweetens the stress of suspiring suspicion that
    sobs in the semblance and sound of a sigh ;
Only this oracle opens Olympian, in mystical moods
    and triangular tenses—
  " Life is the lust of a lamp for the light that is
    dark till the dawn of the day when we
    die."
Mild is the mirk and monotonous music of memory,
    melodiously mute as it may be,
  While the hope in the heart of a hero is bruised
    by the breach of men's rapiers, resigned to the
    rod ;
Made meek as a mother whose bosom-beats bound
    with the bliss-bringing bulk of a balm-breathing
    baby,
As they grope through the graveyard of creeds,
    under skies growing green at a groan for the
    grimness of God.

Blank is the book of his bounty beholden of old, and
    its binding is blacker than bluer :
  Out of blue into black is the scheme of the skies,
    and their dews are the wine of the bloodshed of
    things ;
Till the darkling desire of delight shall be free as a
    fawn that is freed from the fangs that pursue
    her,
  Till the heart-beats of hell shall be hushed by a
    hymn from the hunt that has harried the kennel
    of kings.

THE HIGHER PANTHEISM IN A NUTSHELL
(*Tennyson*)

ONE, who is not, we see ; but one, whom we see
    not, is :
Surely this is not that : but that is assuredly this.

What, and wherefore, and whence ? for under is
    over and under :
If thunder could be without lightning, lightning could
    be without thunder.

Doubt is faith in the main : but faith, on the whole,
    is doubt :
We cannot believe by proof : but could we believe
    without ?

Why, and whither, and how ? for barley and rye are
    not clover :
Neither are straight lines curves : yet over is under
    and over.

Two and two may be four : but four and four are not
    eight :
Fate and God may be twain : but God is the same
    thing as fate.

Ask a man what he thinks, and get from a man what
    he feels :
God, once caught in the fact, shows you a fair pair of
    heels.

Body and spirit are twins : God only knows which
    is which :
The soul squats down in the flesh, like a tinker
    drunk in a ditch.

More is the whole than a part : but half is more than
    the whole :
Clearly, the soul is the body : but is not the body
    the soul ?

One and two are not one : but one and nothing
    is two :
Truth can hardly be false, if falsehood cannot be
    true.

Once the mastodon was : pterodactyls were common
    as cocks :
Then the mammoth was God : now is He a prize
    ox.

Parallels all things are : yet many of these are
    askew :
You are certainly I : but certainly I am not
    you.

Springs the rock from the plain, shoots the stream
    from the rock :
Cocks exist for the hen :   but hens exist for the cock.

God, whom we see not, is : and God, who is not,
    we see :
Fiddle, we know, is diddle : and diddle, we take it,
    is dee.

THE POET AND THE WOODLOUSE
(*E. B. Browning*)

SAID a poet to a woodlouse—" Thou art certainly
    my brother ;
  I discern in thee the markings of the fingers of
    the Whole ;
And I recognize, in spite of all the terrene smut and
    smother,
  In the colours shaded off thee, the suggestions
    of a soul.

" Yea," the poet said, " I smell thee by some passive
    divination,
  I am satisfied with insight of the measure of
    thine house ;
What had happened I conjecture, in a blank and
    rhythmic passion,
  Had the aeons thought of making thee a man,
    and me a louse.

" The broad lives of upper planets, their absorption
    and digestion,
  Food and famine, health and sickness, I can
    scrutinize and test ;

Through a shiver of the senses comes a resonance
    of question,
    And by proof of balanced answer I decide that
    I am best.

" Man, the fleshly marvel, always feels a certain
    kind of awe stick
    To the skirts of contemplation, cramped with
    nympholeptic weight :
Feels his faint sense charred and branded by the
    touch of solar caustic,
    On the forehead of his spirit feels the footprint of
    a Fate."

" Notwithstanding which, O poet," spake the wood-
    louse, very blandly,
    " I am likewise the created,—I the equipose of
    thee ;
I the particle, the atom, I behold on either hand
    lie
    The inane of measured ages that were embryos of
    me.

" I am fed with intimations, I am clothed with
    consequences,
    And the air I breathe is coloured with apocalyptic
    blush ;
Ripest-budded odours blossom out of dim chaotic
    stenches,
    And the Soul plants spirit-lilies in sick leagues
    of human slush.

" I am thrilled half cosmically through by crypto-
          phantic surgings,
     Till the rhythmic hills roar silent through a spon-
          gious kind of blee :
And earth's soul yawns disembowelled of her
          pancreatic organs,
     Like a madrepore if mesmerized, in rapt catalepsy :

" And I sacrifice, a Levite—and I palpitate, a poet ;
     Can I close dead ears against the rush and reso-
          nance of things ?
Symbols in me breathe and flicker up the heights of
          the heroic ;
     Earth's worst spawn, you said, and cursed me ?
          look ! approve me ! I have wings.

" Ah, men's poets ! men's conventions crust you
          round and swathe you mist-like,
     And the world's wheels grind your spirits down
          the dust ye overtrod :
We stand sinlessly stark-naked in effulgence of the
          Christlight,
     And our polecat chokes not cherubs ; and our
          skunk smells sweet to God.

" For He grasps the pale Created by some thousand
          vital handles,
     Till a Godshine, bluely winnowed through the
          sieve of thunderstorms,
Shimmers up the non-existent round the churning
          feet of angels ;
     And the atoms of that glory may be seraphs,
          being worms.

" Friends, your nature underlies us and your pulses
     overplay us ;
  Ye, with social sores unbandaged, can ye sing
     right and steer wrong ?
For the transient cosmic, rooted in imperishable
     chaos,
  Must be kneaded into drastics as material for a
     song.

" Eyes once purged from homebred vapours through
     humanitarian passion
  See that monochrome a despot through a demo-
     cratic prism ;
Hands that rip the soul up, reeking from divine
     evisceration,
  Not with priestlike oil anoint him, but a stronger,
     smelling chrism.

" Pass, O poet, retransfigured !   God, the psycho-
     metric rhapsode,
  Fills with fiery rhythms the silence, stings the
     dark with stars that blink ;
All eternities hang round him like an old man's
     clothes collapséd,
  While he makes his mundane music—AND HE
     WILL NOT STOP, I THINK."

THE PERSON OF THE HOUSE : THE KID
(*Patmore*)

M Y spirit, in the doorway's pause,
    Fluttered with fancies in my breast ;
Obsequious to all decent laws,
  I felt exceedingly distressed.

I knew it rude to enter there
  With Mrs. V. in such a state ;
And, 'neath a magisterial air,
  Felt actually indelicate.
I knew the nurse began to grin ;
  I turned to greet my Love. Said she—
" Confound your modesty, come in !
  —What shall we call the darling, V. ? "
(There are so many charming names !
  Girls'—Peg, Moll, Doll, Fan, Kate, Blanche,
    Bab :
Boys'—Mahershalal-hashbaz, James,
  Luke, Nick, Dick, Mark, Aminadab.)

Lo, as the acorn to the oak,
  As well-heads to the river's height,
As to the chicken the moist yolk,
  As to high noon the day's first white—
Such is the baby to the man.
  There, straddling one red arm and leg,
Lay my last work, in length a span,
  Half hatched, and conscious of the egg.
A creditable child, I hoped ;
  And half a score of joys to be
Through sunny lengths of prospect sloped
  Smooth to the bland futurity.
O, fate surpassing other dooms,
  O, hope above all wrecks of time !
O, light that fills all vanquished glooms,
  O, silent song o'ermastering rhyme !
I covered either little foot,
  I drew the strings about its waist ;
Pink as the unshell'd inner fruit,
  But barely decent, hardly chaste,

Its nudity had startled me ;
  But when the petticoats were on,
" I know," I said ; " its name shall be
  Paul Cyril Athanasius John."
" Why," said my wife, " the child's a girl."
  My brain swooned, sick with failing sense ;
With all perception in a whirl,
  How could I tell the difference ?

" Nay," smiled the nurse, " the child's a boy."
  And all my soul was soothed to hear
That so it was : then startled Joy
  Mocked Sorrow with a doubtful tear.
And I was glad as one who sees
  For sensual optics things unmeet :
As purity makes passion freeze,
  So faith warns science off her beat.
Blessed are they that have not seen,
  And yet, not seeing, have believed :
To walk by faith, as preached the Dean,
  And not by sight, have I achieved.
Let love, that does not look, believe ;
  Let knowledge, that believes not, look :
Truth pins her trust on falsehood's sleeve,
  While reason blunders by the book.
Then Mrs. Prig addressed me thus :
  " Sir, if you'll be advised by me,
You'll leave the blessed babe to us ;
  It's my belief he wants his tea."

Henry S. Leigh (1837–1883)

'TWAS EVER THUS
(*Moore*)

I NEVER rear'd a young gazelle,
  (Because, you see, I never tried);
But had it known and loved me well,
  No doubt the creature would have died.
My rich and aged Uncle John
  Has known me long and loves me well,
But still persists in living on—
  I would he were a young gazelle.

I never loved a tree or flower;
  But, if I had, I beg to say
The blight, the wind, the sun, or shower
  Would soon have withered it away.
I've dearly loved my Uncle John,
  From childhood to the present hour,
And yet he will go living on—
  I would he were a tree or flower!

Anon

FISH HAVE THEIR TIMES TO BITE
(*Mrs. Hemans*)

FISH have their times to bite—
    The bream in summer, and the trout in
  spring,
What time the hawthorn buds are white,
And streams are clear, and winds low-whispering.

The pike bite free when fall
The autumn leaves before the north-wind's breath,
    And tench in June, but there are all—
There are all seasons for the gudgeon's death.

The trout his ambush keeps
Crafty and strong, in Pangbourne's eddying pools,
    And patient still in Marlow deeps
For the shy barbel wait expectant fools.

Many the perch but small
That swim in Basildon, and Thames hath nought
    Like Cookham's pike, but, oh! in all—
Yes, in all places are the gudgeon caught.

The old man angles still
For roach, and sits red-faced and fills his chair;
    And perch, the boy expects to kill,
And roves and fishes here and fishes there.

The child but three feet tall
For the gay minnows and the bleak doth ply
    His bending hazel, but by all—
Oh! by all hands the luckless gudgeon die.

Anon

A PARODY OF HEINE IN SLANG

I SURE wish some guy'd put me jerry
    To what put the jinx on my grin.
Some stuff that's as ancient as Perry
    Is buzzin' around in my bean.

It's time for the glims, and it's chilly,
  There ain't no wild waves on the Rhine;
And, bo, take a slant at that hill. He
  'S lit up like a booze-parlour sign.

A swell-lookin' Jane there is sittin'
  And flashin' a bushel of rocks;
Dolled up in her glad rags, loose fittin'
  She chases the comb thro' her locks.

And while with that 14 K. harrow
  She gives her alfalfa the drag,
She spiels like a white-necktie sparrow
  A classy young raggety-rag.

The guy in his one-lunger dingey
  Goes nuts on her musical game,
And bumps on a rock with a bing. He
  Just can't get his lamps off that dame.

I'll bet you a bone to a marble
  He's going to land in the drink;
And it's Lorelei's fancy old warble
  That put him for keeps on the blink.

Francis Bret Harte (1839–1902)

THE LOST TAILS OF MILETUS
(*E. B. Lytton*)

HIGH on the Thracian hills, half hid in the
  billows of clover,
Thyme, and the asphodel blooms, and lulled by
  Pactolian streamlet,

She of Miletus lay ; and beside her an aged
    satyr
Scratched his ear with his hoof, and playfully
    mumbled his chestnuts.

Vainly the Maenid and the Bassarid gambolled
    about her,
The free-eyed Bacchante sang, and Pan—the re-
    nowned, the accomplished—
Executed his difficult solo. In vain were his gam-
    bols and dances ;
High o'er the Thracian hills, rose the voice of the
    shepherdess, wailing.

" Ai ! for the fleecy flocks, the meek-nosed, the
    passionless faces ;
Ai ! for the tallow-scented, the straight-tailed, the
    high-stepping ;
Ai ! for the timid glance, which is that which the
    rustic sagacious
Applies to him who loves but may not declare his
    passion ! "

Her then Zeus answered low : " O daughter of song
    and sorrow,—
Hapless tender of sheep,—arise from thy long
    lamentation !
Since thou canst not trust fate, nor behave as
    becomes a Greek maiden,
Look and behold thy sheep."   And lo ! they returned
    to her tailless.

Henry Duff Traill (1842–1900)

AFTER DILETTANTE CONCETTI
D. G. Rossetti

" WHY do you wear your hair like a man,
    Sister Helen ?
This week is the third since you began."
" I'm writing a ballad ; be still if you can,
    Little brother.
    (O Mother Carey, mother !
What chickens are these between sea and heaven !)"

" But why does your figure appear so lean,
    Sister Helen ?
And why do you dress in sage, sage green ? "
" Children should never be heard, if seen,
    Little brother !
    (O Mother Carey, mother !
What fowls are a-wing in the stormy heaven !) "

" But why is your face so yellowy white,
    Sister Helen ?
And why are your skirts so funnily tight ? "
" Be quiet, you torment, or how can I write,
    Little brother ?
    (O Mother Carey, mother !
How gathers thy train to the sea from the heaven !) "

" And who's Mother Carey, and what is her train,
    Sister Helen ?
And why do you call her again and again ? "
" You troublesome boy, why that's the refrain,
    Little brother.
    (O Mother Carey, mother !
What work is toward in the startled heaven ?) "

" And what's a refrain ?   What a curious word,
                    Sister Helen !
Is the ballad you're writing about a sea-bird ? "
" Not at all ; why should it be ?   Don't be absurd,
                    Little brother.
        (*O Mother Carey, mother !*
Thy brood flies lower as lowers the heaven.) "

        (*A big brother speaketh :*)
" The refrain you've studied a meaning had,
                    Sister Helen !
It gave strange force to a weird ballad.
But refrains have become a ridiculous ' fad,'
                    Little brother.
        And *Mother Carey, mother,*
Has a bearing on nothing in earth or heaven.

" But the finical fashion has had its day,
                    Sister Helen.
And let's try in the style of a different lay
To bid it adieu in poetical way,
                    Little brother.
        So Mother Carey, mother !
Collect your chickens and go to—heaven."

(*A pause.   Then the big brother singeth, accompany-*
    ing himself in a plaintive wise on the triangle :)

" Look in my face.   My name is Used-to-was ;
    I am also called Played-out and Done-to-death,
    And It-will-wash-no-more.   Awakeneth
Slowly, but sure awakening it has,
The common sense of man ; and I, also !
    The ballad-burden trick, now known too well,
    Am turned to scorn, and grown contemptible—
A too transparent artifice to pass.

" What a cheap dodge I am ! The cats who dart
　Tin-kettled through the streets in wild surprise
　Assail judicious ears not otherwise ;
And yet no critics praise the urchin's ' art,'
Who to the wretched creature's caudal part
　Its foolish empty-jingling ' burden ' ties."

VERS DE SOCIÉTÉ

(*Austin Dobson*)

THERE, pay it, James ! 'tis cheaply earned,
　My conscience ! how one's cabman charges !
But never mind, so I'm returned
　Safe to my native street of Clarges.
I've just an hour for one cigar
　(What style these Reinas have, and what ash !)
One hour to watch the evening star
　With just one Curacao-and-potash.

Ah me ! that face beneath the leaves
　And blossoms of its piquant bonnet !
Who would have thought that forty thieves
　Of years had laid their fingers on it !
Could you have managed to enchant
　At Lord's to-day old lovers simple,
Had Robber Time not played gallant,
　And spared you every youthful dimple !

That robber bold like courtier Claude
　Who danced the gay coranto jesting,
By your bright beauty charmed and awed,
　Has bowed and passed you unmolesting.

No feet of many wintered crows
  Have traced about your eyes a wrinkle ;
Your sunny hair has thawed the snows
  That other heads with silver sprinkle.

I wonder if that pair of gloves
  I won of you you'll ever pay me !
I wonder if our early loves
  Were wise or foolish, Cousin Amy ?
I wonder if our childish tiff
  Now seems to you, like me, a blunder !
I wonder if you wonder if
  I ever wonder if you wonder !

I wonder if you think it bliss
  Once more to be the fashion's leader !
I wonder if the trick of this
  Escapes the unsuspecting reader !
And as for him who does or can
  Delight in it, I wonder whether
He knows that almost any man
  Could reel it off by yards together !

I wonder if—— What's that ? A knock ?
  Is that you, James ? Eh ? What ? God bless
    me !
How time has flown ! It's eight o'clock,
  And here's my fellow come to dress me.
Be quick, or I shall be the guest
  Whom Lady Mary never pardons.
I trust you, James, to do your best
  To save the soup at Grosvenor Gardens.

THE MODERN POET'S SONG
(*Swinburne*)

WHERE hast thou been since battlemented
    Troy
 Rose like a dream to thy loud-stricken lyre?
Why dost thou walk the common earth no more?
Nor lead on high Parnass the Muses' choir
  As when thy Hellas rang from shore to shore
With harpings loud and hymns of holy joy?
Well may we for thy gracious presence long:
  The fashion of the day is classic myth
  And he must liberally deal therewith
Who fain would sing the modern poet's song.

Shake from thy brow the hyacinthine locks
  That hide its ivory splendours! Let thine eyes
Flash forth as blue-white lightnings lubricate,
    Spread sudden day through purple midnight skies
      Or scarlet shafts of dawn illuminate
    The grey and umber of the sleeping rocks!
O colours and O shades of every hue,
  Plain or in combination, faint or strong,
Red green and yellow, black and white and blue,
  How ye assist the modern poet's song!

Far darting Phoibos, lofty Loxias
  (Since thou the glad Greek greeting well mayst
      hear
    That hailed thee erst in Delos the Divine),
  If our late lays have leave to reach thine ear,
Meek, myrtle bearing, give us grace to pass
  Through the white worshippers towards thy
    shrine.

O apt alliteration ! how a throng
   Of self-repeating vowels and consonants,
   How lines of labials, strings of sibilants,
  Make music in the modern poet's song !

I will compare thee to a fowler wight,
   'Snaring the soul with magic-woven words
   Of wondrous music and divinest art ;
Or haply I may liken, heard aright,
   Thy winged strains themselves to captured birds,
   Fast in the meshes of the human heart.
For men and things resemble what we please,
   Such arbitrary powers to bards belong ;
And, in default of genuine similes,
   Conceits will serve the modern poet's song.

Come thou, our lord ; the heart within us dies,
   And, faint, as in a breathless land and bare,
   We take no profit of our piteous day.
   Give us to look upon thee, O most fair ;
Appear, O sweet desire of all men's eyes,
   Ere this dread cup of life shall pass away !
For vague appeals which we interpret not,
   And moody murmurs at unstated wrong,
And aspirations for we say not what,
   Largely compose the modern poet's song.

Come thou, and I my stanzas will illume
   With all the hues that in the rainbow meet,
   Alliterate all letters that there are ;
Out-do all rivals in mysterious gloom,
   Fetch metaphors like magi from afar.
   Lit by no star of meaning, to thy feet.

For these and similar poetic tricks
  Are highly praised our master's school among.
O Swinburne! and O water! how ye mix
  To constitute the modern poet's song.

Punch

A MAUDLE-IN BALLAD
(*Swinburne*)

MY lank limp lily, my long lithe lily,
  My languid lily-love, fragile and thin,
With dank leaves dangling and flower-flap chilly,
That shines like the skin of a Highland gilly!
  Mottled and moist as a cold toad's skin!
    Lustrous and leper-white, splendid and splay!
  Art thou not utter? and wholly akin
  To my own wan soul and my own wan chin,
    And my own wan nose-tip, liked to sway
  The peacock's feather, *sweeter than sin*,
    That I bought for a halfpenny, yesterday!

My long lithe lily, my languid lily,
  My lank limp lily-love, how shall I win!—
Woo thee to wink at me? Silver lily,
How shall I sing to thee, softly, or shrilly?
  What shall I weave for thee—which shall I spin—
    Rondel, or rondeau, or virelay?
  Shall I bee-like buzz, with my face thrust in
  Thy choice, chaste chalice, or choose me a tin
    Trumpet, or touchingly, tenderly play
  On the weird bird-whistle, *sweeter than sin*,
    That I bought for a halfpenny, yesterday?

My languid lily, my lank limp lily,
  My long lithe lily-love, men may grin—
Say that I'm soft and supremely silly—
What care I, while you whisper stilly :
  What care I, while you smile ? Not a pin !
    While you smile, while you whisper—'Tis sweet
      to decay !
    I have watered with chlorodine tears of chagrin,
    The churchyard mould I have planted thee in
      Upside down, in an intense way
    In a round red flower-pot, *sweeter than sin*,
      That I bought for a halfpenny, yesterday.

Andrew Lang (1844–1912)

"OH, NO, WE NEVER MENTION HER"

(*Rossetti*)

L OVE spake to me and said :
    " O lips, be mute ;
Let that one name be dead,
That memory flown and fled,
  Untouched that lute !
Go forth," said Love, " with willow in thy hand,
  And in thy hair
  Dead blossoms wear,
Blown from the sunless land.

" Go forth," said Love, " thou never more shalt see
Her shadow glimmer by the trysting tree ;
  But *she* is glad,
  With roses crowned and clad,
Who hath forgotten thee ! "

But I made answer : " Love !
  Tell me no more thereof,
For she has drunk of that same cup as I.
Yea, though her eyes be dry,
  She garners there for me
  Tears salter than the sea,
Even till the day she die."
So gave I love the lie.

JUBILEE BEFORE REVOLUTION
(*Wm. Morris*)

" TELL me, O Muse of the Shifty, the Man
    who wandered afar,"
So have I chanted of late, and of Troy Burg wasted
  of war—
Now of the sorrows of Menfolk that fifty years have
  been,
Now of the Grace of the Commune I sing, and the
  days of a Queen !
Surely I curse rich Menfolk, " the Wights of the
  Whirlwind " may they—
This is my style of translating, $A\varrho\pi\nu\iota\alpha\iota$—snatch
  them away !
The Rich Thieves rolling in wealth that make profit
  of labouring men,
Surely the Wights of the Whirlwind shall swallow
  them quick in their den !
O baneful, O wit-straying, in the Burg of London
  ye dwell,
And ever of Profits and three per cent. are the tales
  ye tell,

But the stark, strong Polyphemus shall answer you
    back again,
Him whom " No man slayeth by guile and not by
    main."
(By " main " I mean " main force," if aught at all
    do I mean.
In the Greek of the blindfold Bard it is simpler the
    sense to glean.)
You Polyphemus shall swallow and fill his mighty
    maw,
What time he maketh an end of the Priests, the
    Police, and the Law,
And then, ah, who shall purchase the poems of old
    that I sang,
Who shall pay twelve-and-six for an epic in Saga
    slang ?
But perchance even " Hermes the Flitter " could
    scarcely expound what I mean,
And I trow that another were fitter to sing you
    a song for a Queen.

George Thomas Lanigan (1845–1886)

A THRENODY

"The Ahkoond of Swat is dead."—*London Papers.*

WHAT, what, what,
    What's the news from Swat ?
  Sad news,
  Bad news,
Comes by the cable led
Through the Indian Ocean's bed,
Through the Persian Gulf, the Red

Sea and the Med-
Itterranean—he's dead ;
The Ahkoond is dead !

For the Ahkoond I mourn,
    Who wouldn't ?
He strove to disregard the message stern,
    But he Ahkoodn't.
Dead, dead, dead,
    (Sorrow Swats !)
Swats wha hae wi' Ahkoond bled,
Swats whom he hath often led
Onward to a gory bed,
    Or to victory,
      As the case might be,
        Sorrow Swats !

Tears shed,
    Shed tears like water,
Your great Ahkoond is dead !
    That Swats the matter !

Mourn, city of Swat !
Your great Ahkoond is not,
But laid mid worms to rot.
His mortal part alone, his soul was caught
    (Because he was a good Ahkoond)
    Up to the bosom of Mahound.
Though earthy walls his frame surround
(Forever hallowed be the ground !)

And sceptics mock the lowly mound
And say, " He's now of no Ahkoond ! "
    His soul is in the skies,—

The azure skies that bend above his loved
    Metropolis of Swat.
He sees with larger, other eyes
Athwart all earthly mysteries—
    He knows what's Swat.

Let Swat bury the great Ahkoond
    With a noise of mourning and lamentation !
Let Swat bury the great Akhoond
With the noise of the mourning of the
      Swattish nation !

    Fallen is at length
    Its tower of strength,
Its sun is dimmed ere it had nooned ;
Dead lies the great Ahkoond,
    The great Ahkoond of Swat
    Is not !

Arthur Clement Hilton (1851–1877)

OCTOPUS
(*Swinburne*)

STRANGE beauty, eight limbed and eight handed,
  Whence camest to dazzle our eyes ?
With thy bosom bespangled and banded
  With the hues of the seas and the skies ;
Is thy home European or Asian,
  O mystical monster marine ?
Part molluscous and partly crustacean,
      Betwixt and between.

Wast thou born to the sound of sea trumpets?
　　Hast thou eaten and drunk to excess
Of the sponges—thy muffins and crumpets,
　　Of the seaweed—thy mustard and cress?
Hast thou nurtured in caverns of coral,
　　Remote from reproof or restraint?
Art thou innocent, art thou immoral,
　　　　　Sinburnian or Saint?

Lithe limbs curling free as a creeper
　　That creeps in a desolate place,
To enrol and envelop the sleeper
　　In a silent and stealthy embrace;
Cruel beak craning forward to bite us,
　　Our juices to drain and to drink,
Or to whelm us in waves of Cocytus,
　　　　　Indelible ink!

Oh breast that 'twere rapture to writhe on!
　　Oh arms 'twere delicious to feel
Clinging close with the crush of the Python
　　When she maketh her murderous meal!

In thy eight-fold embraces enfolden
　　Let our empty existence escape,
Give us death that is glorious and golden,
　　Crushed all out of shape!

Ah thy red lips, lascivious and luscious,
　　With death in their amorous kiss!
Cling round us and clasp us, and crush us,
　　With bitings of agonised bliss;

We are sick with the poison of pleasure,
  Dispose us the potion of pain ;
Ope thy mouth to its uttermost measure,
        And bite us again !

THE HEATHEN PASS-EE
(Bret Harte)

WHICH I wish to remark,
        And my language is plain,
That for plots that are dark
  And not always in vain,
The Heathen Pass-ee is peculiar,
  And the same I would rise to explain.

I would also premise
  That the term of Pass-ee
Most fitly applies,
  As you probably see,
To one whose vocation is passing
  The " ordinary B.A. degree."

Tom Crib was his name,
  And I shall not deny
In regard to the same
  What that name might imply,
That his face it was trustful and childlike,
  And he had the most innocent eye.

Upon April the First
  The Little-Go fell,
And that was the worst
  Of the gentleman's sell,
For he fooled the Examining Body
  In a way I'm reluctant to tell.

The candidates came
  And Tom Crib soon appeared ;
It was Euclid, the same
  Was " the subject he feared " ;
But he smiled as he sat by the table
  With a smile that was wary and weird.

Yet he did what he could,
  And the papers he showed
Were remarkably good,
  And his countenance glowed
With pride when I met him soon after
  As he walked down the Trumpington Road.

We did not find him out,
  Which I bitterly grieve,
For I've not the least doubt
  That he'd placed up his sleeve
Mr. Todbunker's excellent Euclid,
  The same with intent to deceive.

But I shall not forget
  How the next day or two
A stiff paper was set
  By Examiner U——
On Euripides' tragedy, Bacchae,
  A subject Tom " partially knew."

But the knowledge displayed
  By that Heathen Pass-ee,
And the answers he made
  Were quite frightful to see,
For he rapidly floored the whole paper
  By about twenty minutes to three.

Then I looked up at U——
  And he gazed upon me,
I observed, " This won't do " ;
  He replied, " Goodness me !
We are fooled by this artful young person."
  And he sent for that Heathen Pass-ee.

The scene that ensued
  Was disgraceful to view,
For the floor it was strewed
  With a tolerable few
Of the " tips " that Tom Crib had been hiding
  For the " subject he partially knew."

On the cuff of his shirt
  He had managed to get
What we hoped had been dirt,
  But which proved, I regret,
To be notes on the rise of the Drama,
  A question invariably set.

In his various coats
  We proceeded to seek,
Where we found sundry notes
  And—with sorrow I speak—
One of Bohn's publications, so useful
  To the student of Latin or Greek.

In the crown of his cap
  Were the Furies and Fates,
And a delicate map
  Of the Dorian States,
And we found in his palms, which were hollow,
  What are frequent in palms—that is, dates ;

Which is why I remark,
  And my language is plain,
That for plots that are dark
  And not always in vain,
The Heathen Pass-ee is familiar,
  Which the same I am free to maintain.

Henry Cuyler Bunner (1855–1896)

HOME, SWEET HOME, WITH VARIATIONS

I

(Swinburne)

[*'Mid pleasures and palaces—*]

AS sea-foam blown of the winds, as blossom of
    brine that is drifted
  Hither and yon on the barren breast of the breeze
Though we wander on gusts of a god's breath shaken
    and shifted,
    The salt of us stings, and is sore for the sobbing
    seas.
For home's sake hungry at heart, we sicken in
    pillared porches
    Of bliss, made sick for a life that is barren of
    bliss,
For the place whereon is a light out of heaven that
    sears not nor scorches,
    Nor elsewhere than this.

[*An exile from home, splendour dazzles in vain—*]

For here we know shall no gold thing glisten,
  No bright thing burn, and no sweet thing shine ;
Nor Love lower never an ear to listen
  To words that work in the heart like wine.

What time we are set from our land apart,
For pain of passion and hunger of heart,
Though we walk with exiles fame faints to christen,
  Or sing at the Cytherean's shrine.

[VARIATION : *An exile from home*—]

Whether with him whose head
Of gods is honouréd,
With song made splendent in the sight of men—
  Whose heart most sweetly stout
  From ravished France cast out,
Being firstly hers, was hers most wholly then—
  Or where on shining seas like wine
  The dove's wings draw the drooping Erycine.

[*Give me my lowly thatched cottage*—]

For Joy finds Love grow bitter,
And spreads his wings to quit her,
At thought of birds that twitter
    Beneath the roof-tree's straw—
Or birds that come for calling,
No fear or fright appalling,
When dews of dusk are falling,
    Or daylight's draperies draw.

[*Give me them, and the peace of mind*—]

Give me these things then back, though the giving
  Be at cost of earth's garner of gold ;
There is no life without these worth living,
  No treasure where these are not told.
For the heart give the hope that it knows not,
  Give the balm for the burn of the breast—
For the soul and the mind that repose not,
    O, give us a rest !

II

(*Bret Harte*)

BROWN o' San Juan,
  Stranger, I'm Brown.
Come up this mornin' from 'Frisco—
  Be'n a-saltin' my specie-stacks down.

Be'n a-knockin' around,
  Fer a man from San Juan,
Putty consid'able frequent—
  Jes' catch onter that streak o' the dawn !

Right thar lies my home—
  Right thar in the red—
I could slop over, stranger, in po'try
  Would spread out old Shakspoke cold dead.

Stranger, you freeze to this : there ain't no kinder
    gin-palace,
Nor no variety-show lays over a man's own rancho.
Maybe it hain't no style, but the Queen in the
    Tower o' London
Ain't got naathin' I'd swop for that house over thar
    on the hill-side.

Thar is my ole gal, 'n' the kids, 'n' the rest o' my
    live stock ;
Thar my Remington hangs, and thar there's a
    griddle-cake br'ilin'—
For the two of us, pard—and thar, I allow, the
    heavens
Smile more friendly-like than on any other locality.

Stranger, nowhere else I don't take no satisfaction.
Gimme my ranch, 'n' them friendly old Shanghai
 chickens—
I brung the original pair f'm the States in eighteen-
 'n' fifty—
Gimme them and the feelin' of solid domestic comfort.

  Yer parding, young man—
   But this landscape a kind
  Er flickers—I 'low 'twuz the po'try—
   I thought thet my eyes hed gone blind.
.   .   .   .   .

  Take that pop from my belt!
   Hi, thar—gimme yer han' —
  Or I'll kill myself—Lizzie!—she's left me—
   Gone off with a purtier man!

  Thar, I'll quit—the old gal
   An' the kids—run away!
  I be derned! Howsomever, come in, pard—
   The griddle-cake's thar, anyway.

III

(*Austin Dobson*)

AT home alone, O Nomades,
  Although Maecenas' marble frieze
 Stand not between you and the sky,
 Nor Persian luxury supply
Its rosy surfeit, find ye ease.
Tempt not the far Ægean breeze;
With home-made wine and books that please,
  To duns and bores the door deny
   At home, alone.

Strange joys may lure. Your deities
Smile here alone. Oh, give me these:
　Low eaves, where birds familiar fly,
　And peace of mind, and, fluttering by,
My Lydia's graceful draperies,
　　　At home, *alone*.

IV

(*Goldsmith*)

HOME ! at the word, what blissful visions rise ;
　Lift us from earth, and draw toward the skies !
'Mid mirag'd towers, or meretricious joys,
Although we roam, one thought the mind employs :
Or lowly hut, good friend, or loftiest dome,
Earth knows no spot so holy as our Home.
There, where affection warms the father's breast,
There is the spot of heav'n most surely blest.
Howe'r we search, though wandering with the wind
Through frigid Zembla, or the heats of Ind,
Not elsewhere may we seek, nor elsewhere know
The light of heav'n upon our dark below.

V

(*Pope*)

WHEN from our dearest hope and haven reft,
　Delight nor dazzles, nor is luxury left,
We long, obedient to our nature's law,
To see again our hovel thatched with straw :
See birds that know our avenaceous store
Stoop to our hand, and thence repleted soar :
But, of all hopes the wanderer's soul that share,
His pristine peace of mind's his final prayer.

VI

(*Walt Whitman*)

I

YOU over there, young man with the guide-book
     red-bound, covered flexibly with red linen,
Come here, I want to talk with you ; I, Walt, the
     Manhattanese, citizen of these States, call you.
Yes, and the courier, too, smirking, smug-mouthed,
     with oil'd hair ; a garlicky look about him
     generally ; him, too, I take in, just as I would
     a coyote, or a king, or a toad-stool, or a ham-
     sandwich, or anything or anybody else in the
     world.
Where are you going ?
You want to see Paris, to eat truffles, to have a good
     time ; in Vienna, London, Florence, Monaco,
     to have a good time ; you want to see Venice.
Come with me.   I will give you a good time ; I will
     give you all the Venice you want, and most of
     the Paris.
I, Walt, I call to you.   I am all on deck !   Come
     and loaf with me !   Let me tote you around
     by your elbow and show you things.
You listen to my ophicleide !
Home !
Home, I celebrate.   I elevate my fog-whistle,
     inspir'd by the thought of home.
Come in !—take a front seat ; the jostle of the
     crowd not minding ; there is room enough for
     all of you.
This is my exhibition—it is the greatest show on
     earth—there is no charge for admission.
All you have to pay me is to take in my romanza.

II

1. The brown-stone house ; the father coming home
     worried from a bad day's business ; the
     wife meets him in the marble-pav'd vestibule ;
     she throws her arms about him ; she presses
     him close to her ; she looks him full in the
     face with affectionate eyes ; the frown from
     his brow disappearing.

   Darling, she says, *Johnny has fallen down and
   cut his head ; the cook is going away, and the
   boiler leaks.*

2. The mechanic's dark little third story room, seen
     in a flash from the Elevated Railway train ;
     the sewing-machine in a corner ; the small
     cook-stove ; the whole family eating cabbage
     around a kerosene lamp ; of the clatter and
     roar and groaning wail of the Elevated train
     unconscious ; of the smell of the cabbage
     unconscious.

   Me, passant, in the train, of the cabbage not quite
   so unconscious.

3. The French flat ; the small rooms, all right
     angles, unindividual ; the narrow halls ; the
     gaudy cheap decorations everywhere.

   The janitor and the cook exchanging compliments
   up and down the elevator-shaft ; the refusal
   to send up more coal, the solid splash of the
   water upon his head, the language he sends
   up the shaft, the triumphant laughter of the
   cook, to her kitchen retiring.

4. The widow's small house in the suburbs of the
     city ; the widow's boy coming home from

his first day down town ; he is flushed with happiness and pride ; he is no longer a school-boy, he is earning money ; he takes on the airs of a man and talks learnedly of business.

5. The room in the third-class boarding-house ; the mean little hard-coal fire, the slovenly Irish servant-girl making it, the ashes on the hearth, the faded furniture, the private provender hid away in the closet, the dreary back-yard out the window ; the young girl at the glass, with her mouth full of hair-pins, doing up her hair to go downstairs and flirt with the young fellows in the parlour.

6. The kitchen of the old farm-house ; the young convict just return'd from prison—it was his first offence, and the judges were lenient to him.

He is taking his first meal out of prison ; he has been receiv'd back, kiss'd, encourag'd to start again ; his lungs, his nostrils expand with the big breaths of free air ; with shame, with wonderment, with a trembling joy, his heart too expanding.

The old mother busies herself about the table ; she has ready for him the dishes he us'd to like ; the father sits with his back to them, reading the newspaper, the newspaper shaking and rustling much ; the children hang wondering around the prodigal—they have been caution'd : *Do not ask where our Jim has been ; only say you are glad to see him.*

The elder daughter is there, pale-fac'd, quiet ;

her young man went back on her four years ago ; his folks would not let him marry a convict's sister. She sits by the window, sewing on the children's clothes, the clothes not only patching up ; her hunger for children of her own invisibly patching up.

The brother looks up ; he catches her eye, he fearful, apologetic ; she smiles back at him, not reproachfully smiling, with loving pretence of hope smiling—it is too much for him ; he buries his face in the folds of the mother's black gown.

7. The best room of the house, on the Sabbath only open'd ; the smell of horse-hair furniture and mahogany varnish ; the ornaments on the what-not in the corner ; the wax-fruit, dusty, sunken, sagged in, consumptive-looking, under a glass globe ; the sealing-wax imitation of coral ; the cigar boxes with shells plastered over ; the perforated card-board motto.

The kitchen ; the housewife sprinkling the clothes for the fine ironing to-morrow—it is Third-day night, and the plain things are already iron'd, now in cupboards, in drawers stowed away.

The wife waiting for the husband—he is at the tavern, jovial, carousing ; she, alone in the kitchen sprinkling clothes—the little red wood clock with peaked top, with pendulum wagging behind a pane of gaily painted glass, strikes twelve.

The sound of the husband's voice on the still night air—he is singing : *We won't go home*

till morning !—the wife arising, toward the
    wood-shed hastily going, stealthily entering,
    the voice all the time coming nearer, inebri-
    ate, chantant.

The wood-shed ; the club behind the door of the
    woodshed ; the wife annexing the club ; the
    husband approaching, always inebriate, chan-
    tant.

The husband passing the door of the wood-shed ;
    the club over his head, now with his head in
    contact ; the sudden cessation of the song ;
    the temperance pledge signed the next morn-
    ing ; the benediction of peace over the domes-
    tic foyer temporarily resting.

III

I sing the soothing influences of home.
You, young man, thoughtlessly wandering, with
    courier, with guide-book wandering.
You hearken to the melody of my steam-calliope.
Yawp !

G. H. Powell (18—?–19—?)

OSMUNDA REGALIS ;

OR, HISTORY IN THE SUBJUNCTIVE MOOD

" . . . WE may therefore not unreasonably infer
that it was in the transition period, between the
age of iron savagery which we have just been des-
cribing, and the intellectual quasi-revival of the
ante-Norman period, that a character, whose influence upon the social life and development of our
nation can still be indistinctly traced beneath the

superficial crust of a later civilization, first appeared upon the stage of English history. It would thus be at the very dawn of this brighter age that Osmunda Regalis, to call the abbess by a traditional name, the authenticity of which we shall discuss presently, was probably born—assuming the passage which we have quoted above from the Saxon Chronicle not to be an interpolation—in a smiling valley of one (though we should be hardly justified in saying which) of the most lovely counties of Anglo-Saxon Britain. Without prolonging a barren discussion on the etymology of a name, around which so many respectful associations have clustered, the affectionate student of our national civilization may be allowed to base upon the pretty legend of the ' Os mundum ' a cheering belief that in the darkest ages a woman's ' utterances of pure wisdom ' (and we have no evidence that the Abbess Osmunda was not an eloquent preacher sufficient to cause us to reject even such a highly problematical interpretation of her name) in some way heralded the incoming of what was perhaps after all a more cultivated age than the preceding one. The brief and respectful reference in the pages of Gulielmus Neubrigensis should, it seems probable, be taken to refer at least to the celebrity and learning of some noble Saxon lady of similar name, even if it does not entitle us to place Osmunda herself intellectually at the head of all her contemporaries.

" Amid the ancient cloisters of which a few crumbling ruins now mark—in the opinion of one uncertain archæological authority—the ruins of what was doubtless long known, if it was known at all, as St. Osmund's Nunnery, surrounded by a bevy of maidens, among whom the daughters of a Hengist may well have been found side by side with the ancestors of a Plantagenet, we can picture her at her work,—we can glow with enthusiasm at the picture of the noble spinster, who, it may be, embodied in her striking character all the vigour infused by the Roman invader into the fiery Ibero-Celtic stock (for the Latinization of her name would appear to indicate a mixed parentage), directing the spiritual and material affairs of an abbey, which was perhaps—as why should it not have been ?—a more popular centre of culture and refinement than any inferior institution of the same kind ; teaching, advising, already, it may be, foreseeing the future more free and influential position of her sex, respected by the young ; alike distinguished (may we not believe ?) for her piety and learning, and if so, possibly courted by the most eminent prelates of her day ; although to go further and hazard the conclusion that she was the earliest advocate of the great cause of women's education would be, although under the circumstances not extremely unlikely, perhaps more than a historian could advisably assert. What we need not scruple to state is that such a social phenomenon—such a manifestation of religious and intellectual vitality—would be equally significant whether it took place (a question which our imperfect data hardly enable us to answer with precision) in the ninth, tenth, or eleventh century of this era of disjointed and yet ever continuous human progress.

" Nor would such merit have been, so far as we can judge, unrecognised even at the period—whatever we assume it to be—of which we are speaking,

That the honourable title of ' Regalis,' if it were not
first bestowed as a mere compliment by a chronicler,
as seems not impossible, of some generations later
date, was the symbolic monument of a royal visit at
which some warlike chieftain—the grandson, perchance, of a Northumbrian Heptarch—stooped his
crowned head beneath the rudely-carved portals of
that peaceful sanctum of religion and learning, and
sat at the board of the lady abbess, bestowing upon
his hardly less nobly born hostess such an unusual
honour in lieu of a golden tribute from his treasury,
which, if not securely buried in some rude and impregnable Saxon fortress, was not improbably even
at that moment being plundered by the Danish
pirate ; this would be inconsistent with nothing
which we know of the relations between royal and
ecclesiastical influences in the earliest phases of
mediæval English society. . . .

"All this may be so. But none the less the
traveller of to-day, as he contemplates the waving
woods, the flowing——visible from the grassy emi-
nence of ——, which may well have been on sunny
afternoons the favourite resort of Osmunda, may
still feel that her life-work has not been thrown
idly down the stream of national development, that
we have not quite lost the threads of tradition connecting the political interests and feelings of our
highly-strung modern civilization with the aspirations," etc., etc.

James Kenneth Stephen (1859–1892)

A SONNET
(*Wordsworth*)

TWO voices are there : one is of the deep ;
    It learns the storm-cloud's thunderous
  melody,
Now roars, now murmurs with the changing sea,
Now bird-like pipes, now closes soft in sleep :
And one is of an old half-witted sheep
Which bleats articulate monotony,
And indicates that two and one are three,
That grass is green, lakes damp, and mountains
    steep :
And, Wordsworth, both are thine : at certain times
Forth from the heart of thy melodious rhymes,
The form and pressure of high thoughts will burst :
At other times—good Lord ! I'd rather be
Quite unacquainted with the A B C
Than write such hopeless rubbish as thy worst.

OF R. B.

(*Browning*)

BIRTHDAYS ? yes, in a general way ;
    For the most if not for the best of men :
You were born (I suppose) on a certain day :
So was I : or perhaps in the night : what then ?

Only this : or at least, if more,
You must know, not think it, and learn, not speak :
There is truth to be found on the unknown shore,
And many will find where few will seek.

For many are called and few are chosen,
And the few grow many as ages lapse :
But when will the many grow fat : what dozen
Is fused into one of Time's hammer-taps ?

A bare brown stone in a babbling brook :—
It was wanton to hurt it there, you say :
And the moss, which clung in the sheltered nook
(Yet the stream runs cooler), is washed away.

That begs the question : many a prater
Thinks such a suggestion a sound " stop thief ! "
Which, may I ask, do you think the greater,
Sergeant-at-arms or a Robber Chief ?

And if it were not so ? still you doubt ?
Ah ! yours is a birthday indeed if so.
There were something to write a poem about,
If one thought a little.   I only know.

P.S.

THERE'S a Me Society down at Cambridge,
    Where my works, *cum notis variorum*,
Are talked about ; well, I require the same bridge
That Euclid took toll at as *Asinorum*.

And, as they have got through several ditties
I thought were as stiff as a brick-built wall,
I've composed the above, and a stiff one *it* is,
A bridge to stop asses at, once for all.

Francis Thompson (1859–1907)

WAKE ! FOR THE RUDDY BALL HAS TAKEN FLIGHT

(*Edward FitzGerald*)

I

WAKE ! for the Ruddy Ball has taken flight
    That scatters the slow Wicket of the
       Night ;
And the swift Batsman of the Dawn has driven
Against the Star-spiked Rails a fiery Smite.

Wake, my Beloved ! take the Bat that clears
The sluggish Liver, and Dyspeptics cheers :
    To-morrow ? Why, to-morrow I may be
Myself with Hambledon and all its Peers.

To-day a Score of Batsmen brings, you say ?
Yes, but where leaves the Bats of yesterday ?
    And this same summer day that brings a
       Knight
May take the Grace and Ranjitsinjh away.

Willsher the famed is gone with all his " throws,"
And Alfred's Six-foot Reach where no man knows ;
    And Hornby—that great hitter—his own Son
Plays in his place, yet recks not the Red Rose.

And Silver Billy, Fuller Pilch and Small,
Alike the pigmy Briggs and Ulyett tall,
    Have swung their Bats an hour or two before,
But none played out the last and silent Ball.

Well, let them Perish ! What have we to do
With Gilbert Grace the Great, or that Hindu ?
   Let Hirst and Spooner slog them as they list
Or Warren bowl his " snorter " ; care not you !

With me along the Strip of Herbage strown,
That is not laid or watered, rolled or sown,
   Where name of Lord's and Oval is forgot,
And peace to Nicholas on his bomb-girt Throne.

A level Wicket, as the Ground allow,
A driving Bat, a lively Ball, and thou
   Before me bowling on the Cricket-Pitch—
O Cricket-Pitch were Paradise enow !

II

I listened where the Grass was shaven small,
And heard the Bat that groaned against the Ball :
   Thou pitchest Here and There, and Left and Right,
Nor deem I where the Spot thou next may'st Fall.

Forward I play, and Back, and Left and Right,
And overthrown at once, or stay till Night :
   But this I know, where nothing else I know,
The last is Thine, how so the Bat shall smite.

This thing is sure, where nothing else is sure,
The boldest Bat may but a Space endure ;
   And he who One or who a Hundred hits
Falleth at ending to thy Force or Lure.

Wherefore am I allotted but a Day
To taste Delight, and make so brief a stay ;
   For Meed of all my Labour laid aside,
Ended alike the Player and the Play ?

Behold ; there is an Arm behind the Ball,
Nor the Bat's Stroke of its own Striking all ;
    And who the Gamesters, to what end the Game,
I think thereof our Willing is but small.

Against the Attack and Twist of Circumstance
Though I oppose Defence and shifty Glance,
    What Power gives Nerve to me, and what
        Assaults,—
This is the Riddle. Let dull bats cry " Chance."

Is there a Foe that [domineers] the Ball ?
And one that Shapes and wields us Willows all ?
    Be patient if Thy Creature in Thy Hand
Break, and the so-long-guarded Wicket fall !

Thus spoke the Bat. Perchance a foolish Speech
And wooden, for a Bat has straitened Reach :
    Yet thought I, I had heard Philosophers
Prate much on this wise, and aspire to Teach.

Ah, let us take our Stand, and play the Game,
But rather for the Cause than for the Fame ;
    Albeit right evil is the Ground, and we
Know our Defence thereon will be but lame.

O Love, if thou and I could but Conspire
Against this Pitch of Life, so false with Mire,
    Would we not Doctor it afresh, and then
Roll it out smoother to the Bat's Desire ?

O. Henry (1867–1910)

OPTIONS

(*James Whitcomb Riley*)

" PA lays around 'n' loafs all day
    'N' reads and makes us leave him be.
He lets me do just like I please,
    'N' when I'm bad he laughs at me,
'N' when I holler loud 'n' say
    Bad words 'n' then begin to tease
The cat 'n' pa just smiles, ma's mad
    'N' gives me Jesse crost her knees.
I always wondered why that wuz—
        I guess it's cause
        Pa never does.

" 'N' after all the lights are out
    I'm sorry 'bout it ; so I creep
Out of my trundle bed to ma's
    'N' say I love her a whole heap.
'N' kiss her, 'n' I hug her tight.
    'N' it's too dark to see her eyes.
But every time I do I know
    She cries 'n' cries 'n' cries 'n' cries.
I always wondered why that wuz—
        I guess it's cause
        Pa never does."

Sir Frederick Pollock

ARMORY v. DELAMIRIE
(*Chaucer*)

IN Middlesex, that excellent county,
   there dwelt a little sweep hight Armory,
which clomb and crope in chimneys strait and small,
to earn full scanty living therewithal.
This Armory, one time as he doth fare
sadly about his toil, is haply ware,
looking to earthward, of a glittering thing,
and putteth hand thereto, and lo a ring
with gold ywrought and seemly stones therein.
To know the worth hereof he fain would win,
and bringeth it unto a stall thereby,
where sat a goldsmith, hight Delamirie,
and eke a prentice knave of evil wit :
(I n'ot his name, the book saith nought of it.)
This prentice, then, as he would weigh the ring,
took it in hand, and of his false cunning
hath from the socket done the stones clean out.
Anon he cried, " Master, thereof no doubt,
three halfpence is the worth, there nis no more."
Quod Armory, " Me this misliketh sore ;
give me my jewel back, and fare ye well
with such folk which have will good cheap to sell."
For all his words they gave him for the nones
the socket empty and withouten stones,
and leugh upon him and gan call him thief.
Therefore full wisely telleth he his grief
to men of law, which answered him anon :
" The finder hath lawful possession
for all men, save the very owner's title.
Eke from this master ye shall have requital,

for wrong that servant doth, books techen so,
in master's business, *nocet domino*."
What needeth wordës mo : the suit is brought ;
it falleth every point as thus was taught.
And seeing by this wickedness the stone
was made away, and his worth known to none,
craftsmen there came to show by weight and tale
what gems of best and uttermost avail
might in the compass of that ring be laid ;
with no less damage it should be apaid :
for what man hideth truth in wrongdoing,
against him the law deemeth everything.
Thus hath the justice given doom aright,
and Delamirie goeth in ill plight,
and Armory is joyful of his gain.
The tale is done, there is no more to sain

PASLEY v. FREEMAN
(*The Ballads*)

Videlicet die xxjmo
Feb. Londini supra-
dict; &c.

IT was Pasley came with his felaw
    to London town with wares to
      sell,
    sixteen bags of the fine cochineal,
      for buyers who should like them
        well.

Stood up a buyer and spoke so fair,
    John Christopher Falch he had to
      name :
" Right well me liketh the cochineal
      fine,
      and I will freely buy the same."

" If ye be fain to buy our wares,
   we must wot one thing or ere we
      sell :
ye shall do us to wit if ye be of
      worth,
   a man to trust and credit well.

" For but and the silver and gold
      were paid,
   this day were a day to rue full
      sore :
two thousand pound is not the
      worth,
   nor if ye tell six hundred more."

Appiert per le liver que le cochineal estoit de grand value —viz. : del value £2,634.16.1d.

Joseph Freeman stood up and
      spake :
  " I rede you let the wares be sold,
John Christopher is a man of trust
   for the white silver and eke red
      gold."

They have given their wares to
      John Christopher,
   and set him a day to pay in hand ;
John Christopher's fled o'er the wan
      water
   and left no goods within the land.

A ma entente le fait fuit issint, coment que ceo nest espressement nosme deins le liver.

Pasley is woxen as a man wood,
   to sit still him seemed nothing
      meet ;
said, We'll up and sue this false
      Freeman,
   to do us right for his deceit.

There was Grose the one justice,
   said this was but a lewëd thing,
for where ye find no word of promise,
   no action lieth for bare lesing.

Buller was the other justice,
   said, Here is damage and deceit;
where by word of man be comen these twain,
   the third is, to requite his cheat.

Ashhurst was the third justice,
   said, Though he gain not by the lie,
his malice is yet more curst of kind

   than if he had hope to win thereby.

Lord Kenyon was the chief justice,
   said, Full little is left to tell;
but the fraud was plain and eke the loss,
   and I hold this action lieth well.

So Pasley won that cause as then;
   but merchants had thereof affright,
and have letten ordain in Parliament,
   such words shall have no harm ne might

to hold one bound for his fellow's trust,
   but if they be written in black and white,

SCOTT v. SHEPHERD

(*R. Browning*)

NOW, you're my pupil!
     On the good ancient plan I shall do what I can
For *your* hundred guineas to give *my* law's blue
     pill
(Let high jurisprudence which thinks me and you
     dense
Set posse of cooks to stir new Roman soup ill):
First volume of Smith shall give you the pith
Of leading decision that shows the division
Of action *on case* from plain action of *trespass*
Where to count in assault law benignantly says
     " Pass ! "

Facts o' case first. At Milborne Port
Was fair-day, October the twenty and eight,
And folk in the market like fowls in a crate ;
Shepherd, one of your town-fool sort
(From Solomon's time they call it sport,
Right to help holiday, just make fun louder),
Lights me a squib up of paper and powder
(Find if you can the law-Latin for 't)
And chucks it, to give their trading a rouse,
Full i' the midst o' the market-house.

It happed to fall on a stall where Yates
Sold gingerbread and gilded cates
(Small damage if *they* should burn or fly all) ;
To save himself and said gingerbread loss,
One Willis doth toss the thing across
To stall of one Ryal, who straight on espial

Of danger to *his* wares, of selfsame worth,
Casts it in market-house farther forth,
And by two mesne tossings thus it got
To burst i' the face of plaintiff Scott.
And now 'gainst Shepherd, for loss of eye
Question is, whether *trespass* shall lie.

Think Eastertide past, off crowds and packs
    town
Where De Grey, Chief Justice, and Nares and Black-
    stone
And Gould his brethren are set in banc
In a court full of serjeants stout or lank,
With judgment to give this doubt an end
(Layman hints wonder to counsellor friend,
If *express colour* be visible pigment,
And what's by black patch a-top serjeant's wig
    meant).
Nares leads off, opines with confidence
Trespass well lies and there's no pretence
But who gave squib mischievous faculty
Shall answer its utmost consequence
(*Qui facit per alium facit per se*) :
Squib-throwing a nuisance by statute, too !

Blackstone, more cautious, takes other view,
Since 'tis not all one throw, but an impetus new
Is given to squib by Ryal and Willis,
When *vis* first *impressa* thereon spent and still is ;
In fine, would have justice set mouth firm, not
    sound awry,
But teach forms of action to know each his bound-
    ary.

Gould holds with Nares :—If de Grey pairs ?
That were, odzooks, equipoise, *dignus vindice*
Nodus !   But—" I too on same side faith pin, d'ye
    see,"
So De Grey spake—" For, as I take
It, the consequences all flowed of course
From Shepherd's original wrongful force :
Seen rightly, in this case difference *nil* is
In squib's new diversion by Ryal and Willis,
Whom (against Brother Blackstone, I'm free to con-
    fess it) I
Account not free agents, since merest necessity
Bade cast off live squib to save selves and wares."
For such reasons, concurs with Gould and Nares.
Ergo, " *Postea* to the plaintiff."
Next, digest learned editor's notes,
Mark the refinements, preceptor acquaint if
You've duly mastered cases Smith quotes—
Eh ?—No !   What   says book   here ?   As   I'm
    alive,
" Distinctions, had place in principal case,
Since fifty-two make less ado,
And in fact by Judicature Act,
After November seventy-five,
Last stumps of pleading by final weeding
Are grubbed up and thrown adown wind to per-
    dition :
So, note's omitted in present edition ! "
Well—liquor's out, why look more at old bottle ?
Gulp down with gusto, you that are young,
These new Rules' ferment tastes ill in *my* throttle,
Since Justice, *in nubibus* no more on high sitter,
Descends to speak laymen's vulgar tongue.
So be it !   *Explicit—parum feliciter.*

Sir Owen Seaman

THE SACRED FOUNT

(*Henry James*)

IT superficially might have seemed that to answer
Lady Cheveley's invitation to her daughter's
wedding was a matter that would put no intolerable
strain upon the faculties of discriminative volition.
Yet the accident of foreign travel had brought
about that this formal invitation, found on my
return, constituted my first advertisement of even
so much as Vivien Cheveley's engagement to M.
le Comte Richard Sansjambes. The original question, simplified as it was by public knowledge of
the fact that I regard all ceremonial functions with a
polite abhorrence, had, accordingly, taken on a new
complexity, involving considerations of a high
sociologic interest ; as, notably, whether, and, if
at all, in what form, I should offer the lady my
felicitations.

My obsession by these problems over a space of
four-and-twenty hours was only partially relieved
by contact with the *divertissements* of Piccadilly as
I drove to the Prytaneum Club. To my hansom's
temporary arrest, however, attributable to the
stream of vehicles converging in a transverse sense
at the corner of St. James's Street, I owed an interval of recrudescent deliberation. During that so
tense period I conscientiously—such is the force
of confirmed habit—reviewed all the permissible
methods—and scarce fewer than a round dozen of
variants lay at that moment in my right breast-
pocket—of addressing a woman-friend on the occa-

sion of her betrothal. Always the equivocal detachment of an unrejected bachelor had for me the air of imparting to these crises, poignant enough in themselves, a touch of invidious dilemma. The delicate question why the felicitator himself—to hypothecate his eligibility—had not been a candidate for the lady's heart, a question answerable on the lips of her friends, by a theory of unworthiness, and, on those of her enemies, by one of indifference, remained—unless he chose, as one says, to " give himself away "—incapable of adequate solution.

For myself, it is true, by way of a passable solace in this cornucopious predicament, there was my known prejudice, amounting almost, I am told, to a confessed morbidity, in favour of the celibate state. It was still, however, open to the contention of malice that I, nevertheless, conceivably might have—whereas, in fact, I had *not*—submitted to the lady's charms, had they—as they apparently had *not*—been of a sufficiently overwhelming nature. But this, relatively, was, after all, a trivial embarrassment, mastered, on more occasions, already, than one, by a delicate subtlety of diction, in which I permit myself to take a pardonable pride.

" My dear Miss Vivien," I, recalling the terms of a parallel correspondence, had written, " what brings to you, for whom I entertain a so profound regard, brings, to me also, an exquisite joy." And, again, alternatively, and in a phraseology more instinct with poetry and pith—" I, in your gladness, am myself glad." And, once more, with, I confess, a greater aloofness, yet, at the same time, positing, by implication, a plurality of suitors to select from :

—" Quite indubitably enviable is the man on whom your choice has fallen."

But what complicated the situation and left me hesitant between these and, roughly, some nine other openings, was the reflection that, in point of fact, I had never set eyes on the Count, nor yet even heard—and with this my long absence from England must be charged—the lightest tale of him.   Mightn't it be, after all, a marriage, purely, I asked myself, of convenience ?—wealth, possibly, a title, certainly, exchanged for the asset of youthful bloom ? Mightn't it be—and there was recorded precedent for this—that the man, being French as one gathered, and calling himself by a foreign title—a pretension, commonly, that invited scepticism—had exerted over her some Magic, or even, taking into account both his foreignness and his Counthood, as much as Two Magics ?   Or, again, most deplorable of all, mightn't he have acquired a hold upon her by secret knowledge of some skeleton, as the phrase is, in her private cupboard ; an intrigue, let us daringly say, with a former butler, banished for that delinquency and harbouring vengeance against her house by the revelation of her complicity ?

But here I subconsciously reminded myself that the nicest adepts in abstract psychology may, if they do but sufficiently long address themselves to problems abnormally occult, become the prey of a diseased imagination.   And by great good luck the forward movement of my hansom, now disembroiled from the traffic, which had thrown off something of its congestion, caused a current of air which allowed me, the glass being up, a saner purview of the question.   " When I reach the Prytaneum,

I'll," I said, " look the gentleman up in the *Almanach de Gotha*." This, in fact, had been among the motives, had been, I might even say, the dominating motive, of my visit to the Club.

That atmosphere of considered serenity which meets one at the very portals of the Prytaneum, and is of an efficacy so paramount for the allaying of neurotic disorders, had already relieved the tension of my introspective mood by the time that I had entered the *fumoir* and rung for cigarettes and mineral water. The greeting, familiarly curt, that reached me from an armchair near the fire, was traceable, it appeared, to Guy Mallaby. Here, I was glad to think, I had found a living supplement to the *Almanach*, for I remembered him to have been a friend, some had even said a blighted admirer, of Vivien Cheveley. He had married, whether for consolation or from pique, his cook ; and I now noticed, in a glance that embraced him cursorily, that his girth had, since his marriage, increased by some four to six inches.

It could scarce be more than a rude estimate, viewing the fact that I had no tape-measure about me, an adjunct that I from time to time have found serviceable in cases that, apparently, called for mere psychologic diagnosis ; nor, had I so had, am I convinced that I should, in this instance, have allowed myself the application of it. Simply I moved towards him, and, at the same time, yielding to the usage which a twelve-months' absence requires, held out my hand. He took it with, as I thought, a certain surprise, quickly dissembled, but not, as I repeat, before I'd mentally remarked it.

At any other juncture I should have been closely

tempted to pursue the train of inference suggested by this phenomenon ; but just then, for the moment, I was preoccupied. Besides, anyhow, his initial observation proved his astonishment to be derived from a quite transparent, if not altogether venial, cause. "Been out of town," he asked, "for Christmas ? " I confess that, though I had the good breeding not to betray it, this speech, the tone of which, under ordinary conditions, would not have affected me to the point of regarding it as a truancy beyond the prescribed bounds of gentlemanly casualness, caused me, having regard to the circumstance of my long absence, a calculable pain in my *amour propre*. Never so vividly had not merely the complexity, almost cosmic, of life in the Metropolis, its multiform interests and issues so exigently absorbing, but also the inconspicuousness of the vacuum created by the withdrawal of any single—in this case my own—personality, been forced upon my attention.

Here, again, at any other time, I should have found abundant matter for analysis ; but the entrance of the waiter with my cigarettes and mineral water, one of the former of which I deliberately lighted, recalled me from this inviting diversion. By a natural process of reaction I became cognisant of the necessity, every moment more pressing, of composing an answer to Mallaby's question.

Scarce anything could have been easier than so to impregnate my reply with the truth, whole and unadulterated, as to compel, on his side, an embarrassment which I, for one, should have viewed, in the retrospect, as regrettable. Yet, for a full three-quarters of a minute, towards the latter half of which period it was evident that Mallaby conceived my memory to have strangely lapsed, the temptation possessed me to follow the course I have just indicated. But, in the issue—whether more from a desire to spare his feelings, or, at least as much, because the practice of *finesse*, even in conjunctions of negligible import, has had for me always a conquering fascination, I cannot determine—I, with a terseness sufficiently antiphonal to his own, replied: —" Yes. Monte Carlo."

Then, from an apprehension that he might follow up his inquiries—for my travels had, in actual fact, been confined to Central Asia and the transit there and in an opposite sense—or invite a reciprocal curiosity, on my part, in regard to *his* Christmas, " By the way," I, as if by a natural continuity of thought, added, " who is this Count Richard Sansjambes that is to marry Miss Cheveley ? " At the same time, not to appear too intrigued by the matter in question, I withdrew my cigarette from my mouth, flicked it lightly in air, and then abstractedly replaced it, less the ash.

I'd scarce done asking myself whether I'd formulated my inquiry into the identity of this Sansjambes with an air of sufficient detachment, or, in default of this, had so clearly underlined the suggestion of indifference by my manner of manipulating my cigarette as to assure myself against the possible suspicion, easily avoidable, I had hoped, of a too immediately concerned curiosity, when " Ah ! the fellow without legs ! " replied Mallaby, with, as it, perhaps unwarrantably, seemed to me, a levity so flippant that it might have appalled a controversialist less seasoned by practice than I'd the permissible satisfaction of crediting myself with the reputation of being.

" But you have not then lost it ? " I threw off, on a note of implicit irony.

" Lost what ? " he asked.

" Your old facility, of course, in *jeux d'esprit*," I explained.

" On the contrary," he replied, " my translation of Sansjambes is not more literal than the facts themselves ! "

His answer was so quite what I had not foreseen, that I was surprised, as by a sudden reflex jerk of the muscles, into an unwonted lucidity of diction.

" How did he lose them ? " I asked.

" He didn't ; he never had any to lose ! " Mallaby, with unnecessary brutality, replied. " An early ancestor lost *his* under the walls of Acre. Pre-natal influences affected his first-born, and ever since then the family has had no legs in the direct line."

" But the title ? "—I was still too altogether the sport of surexcitation nicely to weigh my words.

" The gallant ancestor's own choice—prior, naturally, to the birth of his heir—to perpetuate the deed of prowess that won it. And his descendants take it on as a matter of pride."

By this I'd sufficiently recovered my habitual *aplomb* to be in a position, while reserving my perfected conclusions for a less disturbing occasion, to collate, as I sipped my drink, a few notes on the comparative periods of sustained effervescence in the cases, respectively, of Seltzer and Salutaris.

" And the cause you assign to this projected marriage ? " I then, less with a desire for enlightenment, asked, than, my own judgment being made up to the point of finality, to seem to flatter him by an appeal to *his*.

" Oh, there's money, of course," he answered. " But that isn't all. It's the old tale—Eve, apple, curiosity, with a touch of the brute thrown in ! "

You could have knocked me down, in the vulgar phrase, with a feather. Here was Guy Mallaby, immeasurably my unequal in fineness of spirit, laying his fat finger plump on the open offence, while I was still complacently nosing it on a false scent of Womanly Pity. True, he had enjoyed a three-months' start of me in the running down of a mystery that doubled too distractingly on its traces for that instinctive *flair* to which I hitherto had urged a predominant claim ; or was it the cook-wife that had piqued, through the stomach's Sacred Fount, his intellectual appetite ? Gratuitously to admit him my superior on the strength of a forestalled judgment was the last of a quite surprising number of alternatives that just then occurred to me.

" I'm going to look in on Lady Jane," I made evasion.

" She'll, if she's honest, endorse my conjecture ; she's a woman ! " he, without hesitation, observed.

More interestingly stimulated than I could, at the moment, remember to have been by any previous visit to the Prytaneum, I made my way westward down the Mall of St. James's Park, taking the broad boulevard on the left. In the particular atmosphere of exaltation by which I perceived myself to be environed, it was easy to image these widowed avenues in their midsummer fulness, to revive their inarticulate romance, to restore, in the grand style, the pomp of their verdurous pageantry. Oh, there was quite enough of analogy to reclothe a whole Arden of *As you like it*! It was really portentous on what a vista of alluring speculations I'd all but originally stumbled ; virgin forest, in fact, before the temerity of just one pioneer, and that a woman, had stripped it this very summer so pitilessly bare. With how fine an abstraction from the moralities I'd, in the way of pure analysis, have probed its fungus-roots, have dissected its saffron-bellied toads, have sampled its ambiguous spices. And to have utilized a legless abortion for the genius of its under-growths !

But I soon became aware of an appreciable recoil from the initial acerbity of my self-reproach at being anticipated by the author of *Sir Richard Calmady*, when, upon a more meticulous reflection—for, by this time, I'd arrived opposite the footpath leading over the bridge that commands the lake and its collection, recognizably unique, of water-fowl—I'd convinced myself how little of consonance was to be found between this theme and the general trend of my predilections. About the loves of a so ineffable prodigy—and to differentiate them as lawful or lawless didn't, for me, modify the fact of their uni-form repulsiveness—I detected a quality something too preposterously flagrant, an element *un peu trop criant* of pungent indelicacy. It needed only this flash of recognition at once to disabuse me of all regret for having been forestalled in the treatment of a subject of which the narrow scope it offered for the play of hypersensitised subtlety remained the incurably fatal defect.

So immediate, indeed, and so absolute was my mental recovery that I had scarce cleared the façade of Buckingham Palace and addressed myself to what I have, from time to time, regarded as the almost contemptibly easy ascent of Constitution Hill, before I had in mind to rush to the opposite extreme, totally, in fact, to disregard the relation of legs to the question at issue. I won't, I said, allow the hereditary absence of this feature from the Count's *ensemble* to prejudice, one way or another, the solution, which I hope ultimately to achieve, of the original problem, namely, should I, or shouldn't I, offer my congratulations to Vivien Cheveley ? and that second problem, subordinately associated with the first, namely, what form, if any, should those congratulations assume ?

But I was instantly to perceive the superprecipitancy of my revulsion. It imposed itself, and with a clarity past all possible ignoring, that in this matter of the Count's legs the introduction of a new element—or, to be accurate, the withdrawal of an old one so usual as to have been carelessly assumed—was bound, whatever dissimulation was attempted, to command notice. The gentleman's lower limbs were, to an undeniably overwhelming degree, conspicuous, as the phrase runs, by their absence. A fresh condition, as unique as it was unforeseen, had, with a disturbing vitality, invaded what had given promise, in the now remote outset, of being an argument on merely abstract and impersonal lines. For, even if one postulated in the bride the delicatest of motives, a passion, let us assume, to repair a defect of Nature, as much as to say, figuratively, " You that are blind shall see through my eyes," or, more literally, " You, having no legs to speak of, are to find in me a vicarious locomotion," even so a sensitive creature might wince at the suspicion that the language of congratulation was but a stammering tribute to the quality, in *her*, of inscrutable heroism.

And there was still an equal apprehension to deplore, should it appear that it was to an artistic faculty, on the lady's part, capable, imaginatively, of reconstructing, from the fragmentary outlines of his descendant, the originally unimpaired completeness of the gallant ancestor—much as the old moon shows dimly perfect in the hollow of the young crescent—that the Count owed his acceptability in her eyes.

" There it is ! " I said, and at the same moment inadvertently grasped the extended hand of a constable at the corner of Hamilton Place ; " there's no escaping from the obsession of this inexorable fact. It colours the whole abstract problem only a little less irritatingly than, I can well believe, it has coloured the poor Count's existence." And I'd scarce so much as *begun* to exhaust the possible bearings of the case in their absorbing relation to simply *me*, as distinct from the parties more deeply committed and so, presumably, exposed to the impact of yet other considerations.

For, what lent a further complexity to the situation was that, even to suppose me arrived at the conclusion, effectively supported, that *her* motive for this so painfully truncated alliance was commendable, it still left her the liberty, accentuated by the conditions at which I have glanced, to misinterpret *mine* in congratulating her upon it. And if, on the other hand, her engagement were attributable to unworthy or frivolous causes, wouldn't the consciousness of this, on *her* side, give even stronger countenance to a suspicion of mere impertinence on *mine*?

That her motive indeed had been no better than one of curiosity—mother Eve's, in fact, for exploring the apple-tree—was the contention of Mallaby, and by him expressed with so resolved an assurance that it had, as I only now remembered, won me over, at the time, by its convincing probability. Hadn't his confidence even gone the length of claiming Lady Jane as of the same camp? And this recalled for me, what I had temporarily ignored in the so conflicting rush of ideas, the primary objective of my present discursion. I'd overlooked the bifurcation of ways where the traverse to South Audley Street leads in the direction of Lady Jane's house; and now was poising irresolutely before crossing at the convergence of Upper Brook Street and Park Lane.

But after all, I asked myself, was a woman's final word really just the thing I stood in dearest need of in so nice a hesitancy? If *I* was conscious of a certain strain in seeking to confine this incident of freakish abbreviation to its properly obscure place in the picture, would not *she*, with all her sex's reluctance to attack any question from an abstract standpoint, experience an insuperable difficulty in assigning to the Count's deficiency its relative " value "? And mightn't I, in a moment of unguarded gallantry, of simulated deference, let me put it, to her (Lady Jane's) assumption of a larger knowledge of women, or, say, simply a more profound intimacy with the particular woman, be carried away, against what I foresaw, even at this

incipient stage of my reflections, would, in the
event, turn out to be my better judgment, on a veri-
table whirl of grossly material considerations ?   At
worst, after all, there's still, I said, the last resort of
an answer in the third person, declining the wedding
invitation on a plea, strictly untrue, of an earlier
engagement.   Meantime, while so many hitherto
unregarded aspects of the matter called on my in-
telligence for their dues, the fabric of my problem
was, I told myself, of a delicacy too exquisite for——

                    [*Left reflecting on kerbstone.*]

A NOCTURNE AT DANIELI'S

(*R. Browning*)

CARO *mio*, *Pulcinello*, kindly hear my wail
        of woe
Lifted from a noble structure,—late Palazzo Dan-
    dolo.

This is Venice you will gather, which is full of pre-
    cious " stones ",
Tintorettos, picture-postcards, and remains of
    Doges' bones.

Not of these I am complaining ; they are mostly
    seen by day,
And they only try your patience in an inoffensive
    way.

But at night when over Lido rises Dian (that's the
    Moon),
And the vicious *vaporetti* cease to vex the still lagoon ;

When the final *trovatore*, singing something old and
    cheap,
Hurls his *tremolo crescendo* full against my beauty
    sleep ;

When I hear the Riva's loungers in debate beneath
    my bower
Summing up (about 1.30) certain questions of the
    hour ;

Then across my nervous system falls the shrill mos-
    quito's boom
And it's " O, to be in England," where the may is
    on the bloom.

I admit the power of Music to inflate the savage
    breast—
There are songs devoid of language which are quite
    among the best ;

But the present orchestration with its poignant Oboe
    part,
Is, in my obscure opinion, barely fit to rank with
    Art.

Will it solace me to-morrow, being bit in either
    eye,
To be told that this is nothing to the season in
    July ?

Shall I go for help to Ruskin ? Would it ease my
    pimply brow
If I found the doges suffered much as I am suffering
    now ?

If identical probosces pinked the lovers who were
    bored
By the sentimental tinkling of Galuppi's clavi-
    chord ?

That's from Browning (Robert Browning)—I have
    left his works at home,
And the poem I allude to isn't in the Tauchnitz
    tome.

But if memory serves me rightly, he was very much
    concerned
At the thought that in the sequel Venice reaped what
    Venice earned.

Was he thinking of mosquitoes ? Did he mean
    their poisoned crop ?
Was it through ammonia tincture " that the kissing
    had to stop " ?

As for later loves—for Venice never quite mislaid
    her spell—
Madame Sand and dear de Musset occupied my own
    hotel !

On the very floor below me, I have heard the patron
    say,
They were put in No. 13 (No. 36 to-day).

But they parted—" *elle et lui* " did—and it now
    occurs to me
That mosquitoes came between them in this " king-
    dom by the sea."

Poor dead lovers, and such brains, too ! What am
  I that I should swear
When the creatures munch my forehead, taking
  more than I can spare ?

Should I live to meet the morning, should the cli-
  mate readjust
Any reparable fragments left upon my outer crust,

Why, at least I still am extant, and a dog that sees
  the sun
Has the pull of Danieli's den of " lions ", dead and
  done.

Courage ! I will keep my vigil on the balcony till
  day
Like a knight in full pyjamas who would rather run
  away.

Courage ! let me ope the casement, let the shutters
  be withdrawn ;
Let Sirocco, breathing on me, check a tendency to
  yawn.
There's the sea ! and *Ecco l'alba* ! Ha ! (in other
  words) the Dawn !

A BIRTHDAY ODE TO MR. ALFRED AUSTIN
(*A. Austin*)

I

THE early bird got up and whet his beak ;
    The early worm arose, an easy prey ;
This happened any morning in the week,
    Much as to-day.

II

The moke uplift for joy his hinder hoof;
　　Shivered the fancy poodle, freshly shorn;
The prodigal upon the attic roof
　　　　Mewed to the morn.

III

His virile note the cock profusely blew;
　　The beetle trotted down the kitchen tong;
The early bird above alluded to
　　　　Was going strong.

IV

All this of course refers to England's isle,
　　But things were going on across the deep;
In Egypt—take a case—the crocodile
　　　　Was sound asleep.

V

Buzzed the Hymettian bee; sat up in bed
　　The foreign oyster sipping local drains;
The impious cassowary lay like lead
　　　　On Afric's plains.

VI

A-nutting went the nimble chimpanzee;—
　　And what, you ask me, am I driving at?
Wait on: in less than twenty minutes we
　　　　Shall come to that.

VII

The bulbous crowfoot drained his dewy cup;
　　The saxifrage enjoyed a morning crawl;
The ampelopsis slowly sidled up
　　　　The garden wall.

VIII

Her petals wide the periwinkle flung ;
  Blue gentian winked upon unweaned lambs ;
And there was quite a pleasant stir among
    The cryptogams.

IX

May was the month alike in croft and wild
  When—here, in fact, begins the actual tale—
When forth withal there came an infant child,
    A healthy male.

X

Marred was his ruby countenance, as when
  A blushing peony is moist with rain ;
And first he strenuously kicked, and then
    He kicked again.

XI

They put the bays upon his barren crest,
  Laid on his lap a lexicon of rhyme,
Saying—" You shall with luck attain the quest,
    In course of time."

XII

Stolid he gazed, as one that may not know
  The meaning of a presage—or is bored ;
But when he loosed his lips it was as though
    The sea that roared.

XIII

That dreadful summons to a higher place
  He would not, if he could, have spurned away ;
But, being a babe, he had, in any case,
    Nothing to say.

XIV

So they continued—" Yes, on you shall fall
 The laurels ; you shall clamber by and bye
Where Southey sits, where lately sat withal
   The Poet Pye.

XV

" As yet you are not equal to the task ;
 A sense of euphony you still must lack ;
Nor could you do your duty by the cask
   Of yearly sack.

XVI

" Just now, withal (that's twice we've said ' withal ')
 The place is filled by someone sitting there;
Yet poets pass ; he, too, will leave his stall
   And go elsewhere.

XVII

" Meanwhile, to trust you with a pointed pen,
 Dear babe, would manifestly be absurd ;
Besides all well-conducted little men
   Are seen, not heard.

XVIII

" First, how to tutor your prehensile mind
 Shall be the object of our deep concern ;
We'll teach you grammar ; *grammar, you will find,*
   Takes years to learn.

XIX

" 'Twixt—mark the pretty word—'twixt boy and
  man
 You shall collate from every source that's known
A blended style ; which may be better than
   One of your own.

XX

" Your classic mould shall be completely mixed
   Of Rome's robustness and the grace of Greece ;
And you shall be a Tory, planted 'twixt
      Plenty and peace.

XXI

" And lo ! we call you Alfred ! Kinglihood
   Lies in the name of Him, the Good and Great !
You may not rise to greatness ; O be good
      At any rate ! "

XXII

Eight happy summers passed and Southey too,
   And one that had the pull in point of age
Walked in ; for Alfred still was struggling through
      The grammar-stage.

XXIII

When William followed out in Robert's wake,
   An alien Alfred filled the vacant spot,
Possibly by some clerical mistake,
      Possibly not.

XXIV

Our friend had then achieved but fifteen years,
   Nor yet against him was there aught to quote ;
For he had uttered in the nation's ears
      Not half a note.

XXV

Adult, no more he dreamed the laurel-wreath,
   But wandered, being credentialled to the Bar,
There where the Northern Circuit wheels beneath
      The polar star.

XXVI

One day, asleep in Court, Apollo's crown
  All in a briefless moment his he saw ;
Then cast his interloping wig adown
      And dropped the Law.

XXVII

Henceforth with loyal pen he laboured for
  His England (situated on the main) ;
Wrote in the tragic, or satiric, or
      Some other vein.

XXVIII

At forty-one he let his feelings go :—
  " If he, that other Alfred, ever die,
And I am not appointed, I will know
      The reason why ! "

XXIX

Some sixteen further autumns bound their sheaves ;
  With hope deferred wild battle he had waged,
And written books. At last the laurel-leaves
      Were disengaged.

XXX

Felicitations, bursting through his bowers,
  Came on him hoeing roots. With mild surprise,
" Leave me alone," he said, " among my flowers
      To botanize."

XXXI

The Prime Elector, Man of Many Days,
  Though Allan's Muse adorned the Liberal side,
Seizing the swift occasion, left the bays
      Unoccupied.

XXXII

The Peer that followed, having some regard
  For humour hitherto accounted sin,
Produced a knighthood for the blameless bard
        Of proud Penbryn.

XXXIII

At length a callous Tory Chief arose,
  Master of caustic jest and cynic gibe,
Looked round the Carlton Club and lightly chose
        Its leading scribe.

XXXIV

And so with heaving heart and happy tears
  Our patient Alfred took the tardy spoil,
Though spent with sixty venerable years
        Of virtuous toil.

XXXV

And ever, when marsh-marigolds are cheap,
  And new potatoes crown the death of May,
If memory serve us, we propose to keep
        His natal day.

THOUGHTS

(*Mrs. Meynell*)

DETACHED in his equilibrium, the Young
Child is instinct with the ichor of Spring.
He flushes a rhythmic pink, the implicit Colour
of Life.

   .   .   .   .

  The vital movement of grass is toward reticence
rather than greenness. By the highways you shall

see its embroidery, a mute protest to shame the scarlet resonance of the pillar-box. That is why the vestries will not have it so.

.   .   .   .

To the glazed eye, dull with yearlong routine, Yarmouth brings relief with the bronze of her kippers. On your seaward breakfast-table they lie, a point of diurnal pungency ; eloquent, too, of suggestion. Salt, that was the breath of their life, is the stuff of their embalming. Not here, in the trite phrase, was death the cure of ill, save for a brief interspace. Then that which gave its savour to existence was itself made the cure of death, last ill of all.

That is why Yarmouth, for all its pier and sable minstrelsy, is still the inviolable hermitage of tired hearts. Its salt is something better than Attic. It breathes, as Athens never wholly breathed in her prime, the continuity of existence. It is vocal with the rhythm of death cured and corrected.

.   .   .

Khaki has the colour of secretiveness ; but the robin wears a cuirass that recalls the published blood. Yet is there also a privacy of the woods, where the bird takes on the tone of his environment. The ancients felt this when they discovered a note of khaki in the flutings of Philomel.

.   .   .   .

Seen in perspective there is symmetry even in the suburb, futile else. Peckham has this dominant note.

Sir Arthur Quiller-Couch

THE NEW BALLAD OF SIR PATRICK SPENS
(*Old Border Ballad*)

THE King sits in Dumferline toun
    Drinking the blude-red wine :
" O wha will rear me an equilateral triangle
    Upon a given straight line ? "

O up and spake an eldern knight
    Sat at the King's right knee—
" Of a' the clerks by Granta side
    Sir Patrick bears the gree.

" 'Tis he was taught by the Tod-huntère
    Tho' not at the tod-hunting ;
Yet gif that he be given a line
    He'll do as brave a thing."

Our King has written a braid letter
    To Cambrigge or thereby
And there it found Sir Patrick Spens
    Evaluating π

He hadna warked his quotient
    A point but barely three,
There stepped to him a little foot-page
    And louted on his knee.

The first word that Sir Patrick read
    " Plus X " was a' he said :
The neist word that Sir Patrick read
    'Twas " *plus* expenses paid."

The last word that Sir Patrick read
  The tear blinded his e'e :
" The pound I most admire is not
  In Scottish currencie."

Stately stepped he east the wa',
  And stately stepped he north ;
He fetched a compass frae his ha'
  And stood beside the Forth.

Then gurly grew the waves o' Forth
  And gurlier by-and-bye—
" O never yet was sic a storm
  Yet it isna sic as I ! "

Syne he had crossed the Firth o' Forth
  Until Dumferline toun
And tho' he came with a kittle wame
  Fu' low he louted down.

" A line, a line, a gude straight line,
  O King, purvey me quick !
And see it be of thilka kind
  That's neither braid nor thick."

" Nor thick nor braid ? " King Jamie said,
  " I'll eat my gude hatband
If arra line as ye define
  Be found in our Scotland."

" Tho' there be nane in a' thy rule
  It sall be ruled by me " ;
And lichtly with his little pencil
  He's ruled the line A B.

Stately stepped he east the wa',
  And stately stepped he west;
" Ye touch the button," Sir Patrick said,
  " And I sall do the rest."

And he has set his compass foot
  Until the centre A,
From A to B he's stretched it oot—
  " Ye Scottish carles, give way ! "

Syne he has moved his compass foot
  Until the centre B,
From B to A he's stretched it oot,
  And drawn it viz-a-vee.

The ane circle was B C D,
  And A C E the tither.
" I rede ye well," Sir Patrick said,
  " They interseck ilk ither.

" See here, and where they interseck—
  To wit with yon point C—
Ye'll just obsairve that I conneck
  The twa points A and B.

" And there ye have a little triangle
  As bonny as e'er was seen ;
The whilk is not isosceles,
  Nor yet it is scalene."

" The proof ! the proof ! " King Jamie cried :
  " The how and eke the why ! "
Sir Patrick laughed within his beard—
  " 'Tis *ex hypothesi*—

" When I ligg'd in my mither's wame
　　I learn'd it frae my mither,
That things was equal to the same
　　Was equal ane to t'ither.

" Sith in the circle first I drew
　　The lines B A, B C,
Be radii true, I wit to you
　　The baith maun equal be.

" Likewise and in the second circle
　　Whilk I drew widdershins
It is nae skaith the radii baith
　　A B, A C, be twins.

" And sith of three a pair agree
　　That ilk suld equal ane,
By certes they maun equal be
　　Ilk unto ilk by-lane."

" Now by my faith ! " King Jamie saith,
　　" What *plane* geometrie !
If only Potts had written in Scots,
　　How loocid Potts would be ! "

" Now, wow's my life ! " saith Jamie the King,
　　And the Scots lords said the same,
For but it was that envious knicht
　　Sir Hughie o' the Graeme.

" Flim-flam, flim-flam ! " and " Ho-indeed ? "
　　Quod Hughie o' the Graeme ;
" 'Tis I could better upon my heid
　　This prabblin prablem-game."

Sir Patrick Spens was nothing laith
  When as he heard " flim-flam,"
But syne he's ta'en a silken claith
  And wiped his diagram.

" Gif my small feat may better'd be ;
  Sir Hew, by thy big head,
What I hae done with an A B C
  Do thou with X Y Z."

Then sairly sairly swore Sir Hew,
  And loudly laucht the King ;
But Sir Patrick tuk the pipes and blew,
  And *played* that eldritch thing !

He's play'd it reel, he's play'd it jig,
  And the baith alternative ;
And he's danced Sir Hew to the Asses' Brigg,
  That's Proposition Five.

And there they've met and there they've fet,
  Forenenst the Asses' Brigg,
And waefu', waefu' was the fate
  That gar'd them there to ligg.

For there Sir Patrick's slain Sir Hew
  And Sir Hew, Sir Patrick Spens.
Now was not that a fine to-do
  For Euclid's Elemen's ?

But let us sing Long live the King !
  And his foes the Deil attend 'em :
For he has gotten his little triangle,
  Quod erat faciendum !

A LETTER

(*W. M. Praed*)

D EAR KITTY,
 At length the term's ending;
 I'm in for my Schools in a week;
And the time that at present I'm spending
 On you should be spent upon Greek.
But I'm fairly well read in my Plato,
 I'm thoroughly red in the eyes,
And I've almost forgotten the way to
 Be healthy and wealthy and wise.
So " the best of all ways "—why repeat you,
 The verse at 2.30 a.m.,
When I'm stealing an hour to entreat you,
 Dear Kitty, to come to Commem. ?

Oh, come ! You shall rustle in satin
 Through halls where examiners trod :
Your laughter shall triumph o'er Latin
 In lecture-room, garden, and quad.
They stand in the silent Sheldonian—
 Our orators, waiting—for you,
Their style guaranteed Ciceronian,
 Their subject—" The Ladies in Blue."
The Vice sits arrayed in his scarlet :
 He's pale but they say he dissem-
bles by calling his Beadle a " varlet "
 Whenever he thinks of Commem.

There are dances, flirtations at Nuneham
 Flower-shows, the procession of Eights :
There's a list stretching *usque ad Lunam*
 Of concerts and lunches and fêtes :

There's the Newdigate all about Gordon,
  —So sweet, and they say it will scan :
You shall flirt with a Proctor, a Warden
  Shall run for your shawl and your fan.
They are sportive as gods broken loose from
  Olympus and yet very em-
inent men. There are plenty to choose from,
  You'll find if you come to Commem.

I know your excuses : Red Sorrel
  Has stumbled and broken her knees ;
Aunt Phoebe thinks waltzing immoral ;
  And, " Algy, you are such a tease ;
It's nonsense, of course, but she *is* strict " ;
  And little Dick Hodge has the croup,
And there's no one to visit your " district "
  Or make Mother Tettleby's soup.
Let them cease for a se'nnight to plague you :
  Oh, leave them to manage *pro tem.*,
With their croup and their soups and their ague,
  Dear Kitty, and come to Commem.

Don't tell me Papa has lumbago,
  That you haven't a frock fit to wear,
That the curate " has notions and may go
  To lengths if there's nobody there,"
That the Squire has " said things " to the Vicar,
  And the Vicar " had words " with the Squire,
That the Organist's taken to liquor,
  And leaves you to manage the choir :
For Papa must be cured, and the curate
  Coerced, and your gown is a gem ;
And the moral is—Don't be obdurate,
  Dear Kitty, but come to Commem.

"My gown?   Though, no doubt, sir, you're clever,
   You'd better leave fashions alone.
Do you think that a frock lasts for ever?"
   Dear Kitty, I'll grant you have grown;
But I thought of my "scene" with McVitie
   That night when he trod on your train
At the Bachelors' Ball.   "'Twas a pity,"
   You said, but I knew 'twas Champagne.
And your gown was enough to compel me
   To fall down and worship its hem—
(Are "hems" wearing?   If not, you shall tell
    me
   What is, when you come to Commem.)

Have you thought, since that night, of the
    Grotto?
   Of the words whispered under the palms,
While the minutes flew by and forgot to
   Remind us of Aunt and her qualms?
Of the stairs of the old *Journalisten*?
   Of the rose that I begged from your hair?
When you turned and I saw something glisten—
   Dear Kitty, don't frown; it was there.
But that idiot Delane in the middle
   Bounced in with "Our dance, I—ahem!"
And—the rose you may find in my Liddell
   And Scott, when you come to Commem.

Then Kitty, let "yes" be the answer.
   We'll dance at the 'Varsity Ball,
And the morning shall find you a dancer
   In Christ Church or Trinity Hall.

And perhaps, when the elders are yawning
   And rafters grow pale overhead
With the day, there shall come with its dawning
   Some thought of that sentence unsaid,
Be it this, be it that—" I forget or
   Was joking "—whatever the fem-
inine fib, you'll have made me your debtor
   And come,—you will come ? to Commem.

TITANIA
(Lord Tennyson)

SO bluff Sir Leolin gave the bride away ;
   And when they married her, the little church
Had seldom seen a costlier ritual.
The coach and pair alone were two-pound ten,
And two-pound-ten apiece the wedding cakes ;—
Three wedding-cakes. A Cupid poised a-top
Of each hung shivering to the frosted loves
Of two fond cushats on a field of ice,
As who should say " *I* see you ! "—Such the joy
When English-hearted Edwin swore his faith
With Mariana of the Moated Grange.

For Edwin, plump head-waiter at The Cock,
Grown sick of custom, spoilt of plenitude,
Lacking the finer wit that saith, " I wait,
They come ; and if I make them wait, they go,"
Fell in a jaundiced humour petulant-green,
Watched the dull clerk slow-rounding to his cheese,
Flicked a full dozen flies that flecked the pane—
All crystal-cheated of the fuller air,
Blurted a free " Good-day t'ye ", left and right,
And shaped his gathering choler to this head :—

" Custom ! And yet what profit of it all ?
The old order changeth yielding place to new,
To me small change, and this the Counter-change
Of custom beating on the selfsame bar—
Change out of chop. Ah me ! the talk, the tip,
The would-be-evening should-be-mourning suit,
The forged solicitude for petty wants
More petty still than they,—all these I loathe,
Learning they lie who feign that all things come
To him that waiteth. I have waited long,
And now I go, to mate me with a bride
Who is aweary waiting, even as I ! "

But when the amorous moon of honeycomb
Was over, ere the matron-flower of Love—
Step-sister of To-morrow's marmalade—
Swooned scentless, Mariana found her lord
Did something jar the nicer feminine sense
With usage, being all too fine and large,
Instinct of warmth and colour, with a trick
Of blunting " Mariana's " keener edge
To " Mary Ann "—the same but not the same :
Whereat she girded, tore her crisped hair,
Called him " Sir Churl," and ever calling " Churl ! "
Drave him to Science, then to Alcohol,
To forge a thousand theories of the rocks,
Then somewhat else for thousands dewy cool,
Wherewith he sought a more Pacific isle
And there found love, a duskier love than hers.

A. E. Housman

FRAGMENT OF A GREEK TRAGEDY

Alcmoen.   *Chorus*

CHO. O suitably-attired-in-leather-boots
    Head of a traveller, wherefore seeking whom
    Whence by what way how purposed art thou
        come
    To this well-nightingaled vicinity ?
    My object in enquiring is to know.
    But if you happen to be deaf and dumb
    And do not understand a word I say,
    Then wave your hand, to signify as much.

ALC. I journeyed hither a Bœotian road.

CHO. Sailing on horseback, or with feet for oars ?

ALC. Plying with speed my partnership of legs.

CHO. Beneath a shining or a rainy Zeus ?

ALC. Mud's sister, not himself, adorns my shoes.

CHO. To learn your name would not displease me
    much.

ALC. Not all that men desire do they obtain.

CHO. Might I then hear at what your presence
    shoots ?

ALC. A shepherd's questioned mouth informed me
    that—

CHO. What ? for I know not yet what you will
    say—

ALC. Nor will you ever, if you interrupt.

CHO. Proceed, and I will hold my speechless tongue.

ALC. —This house was Eriphyla's, no one's else.

CHO. Nor did he shame his throat with hateful
    lies.

ALC. May I then enter, passing through the door ?

CHO. Go, chase into the house a lucky foot.
　　　And, O my son, be, on the one hand, good,
　　　And do not, on the other hand, be bad ;
　　　For that is very much the safest plan.
ALC. I go into the house with heels and speed.

Chorus

In speculation　　　　　　　　　　　*Strophe*
I would not willingly acquire a name
　　For ill-digested thought ;
　　But after pondering much
To this conclusion I at last have come :
　　Life is uncertain.
　　This truth I have written deep
　　In my reflective midriff
　　On tablets not of wax,
Nor with a pen did I inscribe it there,
For many reasons : *Life, I say, is not*
　　A stranger to uncertainty.
Not from the flight of omen-yelling fowls
　　This fact did I discover.
Nor did the Delphic tripod bark it out,
　　Nor yet Dodona.
Its native ingenuity sufficed
　　My self-taught diaphragm.

Why should I mention　　　　　　*Antistrophe*
The Inachean daughter, loved of Zeus ?
　　Her whom of old the gods,
　　More provident than kind,
Provided with four hoofs, two horns, one tail,
　　A gift not asked for
　　And sent her forth to learn

The unfamiliar science
Of how to chew the cud.
She therefore, all about the Argive fields,
Went cropping pale green grass and nettle-tops,
  Nor did they disagree with her.
But yet, howe'er nutritious, such repasts
  I do not hanker after :
Never may Cypris for her seat select
  My dappled liver !
Why should I mention Io ?   Why indeed ?
  I have no notion why.

But now does my boding heart,   *Epode*
  Unhired, unaccompanied, sing
A strain not meet for the dance.
Yea even the palace appears
To my yoke of circular eyes
(The right, nor omit I the left)
Like a slaughterhouse, so to speak,
Garnished with woolly deaths
And many shipwrecks of cows.
I therefore in a Cissian strain lament ;
  And to the rapid,
Loud, linen-tattering thumps upon my chest
  Resounds in concert
The battering of my unlucky head.

ERIPHYLA (*within*). O, I am smitten with a
      hatchet's jaw ;
    And that in deed and not in word alone.
CHO. I thought I heard a sound within the house
    Unlike the voice of one that jumps for joy.
ERI. He splits my skull, not in a friendly way,
    One more : he purposes to kill me dead.

Cho. I would not be reputed rash, but yet
  I doubt if all be gay within the house.
Eri. O! O! another stroke! that makes the
   third.
  He stabs me to the heart against my wish.
Cho. If that be so, thy state of health is poor;
  But thine arithmetic is quite correct.

Anthony C. Deane

JACK AND JILL
(*Rudyard Kipling*)

Here is the tale—and you must make the most of it!
Here is the rhyme—ah, listen and attend!
Backwards—forwards—read it all and boast of it
If you are anything the wiser at the end!

NOW Jack looked up—it was time to sup, and
  the bucket was yet to fill,
And Jack looked round for a space and frowned,
  then beckoned his sister Jill,
And twice he pulled his sister's hair, and thrice he
  smote her side;
"Ha' done, ha' done with your impudent fun—ha'
  done with your games!" she cried:
"You have made mud pies of a marvellous size—
  finger and face are black,
You have trodden the Way of the Mire and Clay—
  now up and wash you, Jack!
Or else, or ever we reach our home, there waiteth an
  angry dame—
Well you know the weight of her blow—the supperless open shame!

Wash, if you will, on yonder hill—wash, if you will,
    at the spring,—
Or keep your dirt, to your certain hurt, and an immi-
    nent walloping ! ''

" You must wash—you must scrub—you must
    scrape ! '' growled Jack, " you must traffic
    with cans and pails,
Nor keep the spoil of the good brown soil in the rim
    of your finger-nails !
The morning path you must tread to your bath—
    you must wash ere the night descends,
And all for the cause of conventional laws and the
    soapmakers' dividends !
But if 'tis sooth that our meal in truth depends on
    our washing, Jill,
By the sacred light of our appetite—haste—haste
    to the top of the hill ! ''
They have trodden the Way of the Mire and Clay,
    they have toiled and travelled far,
They have climbed to the brow of the hill-top now,
    where the bubbling fountains are,
They have taken the bucket and filled it up—yea,
    filled it up to the brim ;
But Jack he sneered at his sister Jill, and Jill she
    jeered at him :
" What, blown already ! '' Jack cried out (and his
    was a biting mirth !)
" You boast indeed of your wonderful speed—but
    what is the boasting worth ?
Now, if you can run as the antelope runs, and if
    you can turn like a hare,
Come, race me, Jill, to the foot of the hill—and
    prove your boasting fair ! ''

" Race ?   What is a race " (and a mocking face had
    Jill as she spoke the word)

" Unless for a prize the runner tries ?   The truth
    indeed ye heard,

For I can run as the antelope runs, and I can turn
    like the hare :

The first one down wins half-a-crown—and I will
    race you there ! "

" Yea, if for the lesson that you will learn (the lesson
    of humbled pride)

The price you fix at two-and-six, it shall not be
    denied ;

Come, take your stand at my right hand, for here is
    the mark we toe :

Now, are you ready, and are you steady ?   Gird up
    your petticoats !   Go ! "

And Jill she ran like a winging bolt, a bolt from the
    bow released,

But Jack like a stream of the lightning gleam, with
    its pathway duly greased ;

He ran down hill in front of Jill like a summer light-
    ning flash—

Till he suddenly tripped on a stone, or slipped, and
    fell to the earth with a crash.

Then straight did rise on his wondering eyes the
    constellations fair,

Arcturus and the Pleiades, the Greater and Lesser
    Bear,

The swirling rain of a comet's train he saw, as he
    swiftly fell—

And Jill came tumbling after him with a loud trium-
    phant yell :

" You have won, you have won, the race is done !
    And as for the wager laid—
You have fallen down with a broken crown—the
    half-crown debt is paid ! "
They have taken Jack to the room at the back
    where the family medicines are,
And he lies in bed with a broken head in a halo of
    vinegar ;
While, in that Jill had laughed her fill as her brother
    fell to earth,
She has felt the sting of a walloping—she hath paid
    the price of her mirth !

Here is the tale—and now you have the whole of it,
    Here is the story—well and wisely planned,
Beauty—Duty—these make up the soul of it—
    But ah, my little readers, will you mark and under-
        stand ?

AN ODE
(*Alfred Austin*)

I SING a song of sixpence, and of rye
    A pocketful—recalling, sad to state,
The niggardly emoluments which I
    Receive as Laureate !

Also I sing of blackbirds—in the mart
    At four-a-penny. Thus, in other words,
The sixpence which I mentioned at the start
    Purchased two dozen birds.

So four-and-twenty birds were deftly hid—
    Or shall we say, were skilfully concealed ?—
Within the pie-dish. When they raised the lid,
    What melody forth pealed !

Now I like four-and-twenty blackbirds sing,
  With all their sweetness, all their rapture keen ;
And isn't this a pretty little thing
  To set before the Queen ?

The money-counting monarch—sordid man !—
  His wife, who robbed the little busy bees,
I disregard. In fact a poet can
  But pity folks like these.

The maid was in the garden. Happy maid !
  Her choice entitles her to rank above
Master and Mistress. Gladly she surveyed
  The Garden That I Love !

—Where grow my daffodils, anemones,
  Tulips, auriculas, chrysanthemums,
Cabbages, asparagus, sweet peas,
  With apples, pears, and plums—

(That's a parenthesis. The very name
  Of " garden " really carries one astray !)
But suddenly a feathered ruffian came,
  And stole her nose away.

Eight stanzas finished ! So my Court costume
  I lay aside : the Laureate, I suppose,
Has done his part ; the man may now resume
  His journalistic prose.

Max Beerbohm

SCRUTS

(*Arnold Bennett*)

I

EMILY WRACKGARTH stirred the Christmas
pudding till her right arm began to ache. But
she did not cease for that. She stirred on till her
right arm grew so numb that it might have been the
right arm of some girl at the other end of Bursley.
And yet something deep down in her whispered
" It is *your* right arm ! And you can do what you
like with it ! "

She did what she liked with it. Relentlessly she
kept it moving till it reasserted itself as the arm of
Emily Wrackgarth, prickling and tingling as with
red-hot needles in every tendon from wrist to
elbow. And still Emily Wrackgarth hardened her
heart.

Presently she saw the spoon no longer revolving,
but wavering aimlessly in the midst of the basin.
Ridiculous ! This must be seen to ! In the down
of dark hairs that connected her eyebrows there
was a marked deepening of that vertical cleft which,
visible at all times, warned you that here was a
young woman not to be trifled with. Her brain
despatched to her hand a peremptory message—
which miscarried. The spoon wobbled as though
held by a baby. Emily knew that she herself as a
baby had been carried into this very kitchen to stir
the Christmas pudding. Year after year, as she
grew up, she had been allowed to stir it " for luck."

And those, she reflected, were the only cookery lessons she ever got. How like Mother!

Mrs. Wrackgarth had died in the past year, of a complication of ailments. Emily still wore on her left shoulder that small tag of crape which is as far as the Five Towns go in the way of mourning. Her father had died in the year previous to that, of a still more curious and enthralling complication of ailments. Jos, his son, carried on the Wrackgarth Works, and Emily kept house for Jos. She with her own hand had made this pudding. But for her this pudding would not have been. Fantastic! Utterly incredible! And yet so it was. She was grown-up. She was mistress of the house. She could make or unmake puddings at will. And yet she was Emily Wrackgarth. Which was absurd.

She would not try to explain, to reconcile. She abandoned herself to the exquisite mysteries of existence. And yet in her abandonment she kept a sharp look-out on herself, trying fiercely to make head or tail of her nature. She thought herself a fool. But the fact that she thought so was for her a proof of adult sapience. Odd! She gave herself up. And yet it was just by giving herself up that she seemed to glimpse sometimes her own inwardness. And these bleak revelations saddened her. But she savoured her sadness. It was the wine of life to her. And for her sadness she scorned herself, and in her conscious scorn she recovered her self-respect.

It is doubtful whether the people of southern England have even yet realized how much introspection there is going on all the time in the Five Towns.

Visible from the window of the Wrackgarths'
parlour was that colossal statue of Commerce which
rears itself aloft at the point where Oodge Lane is
intersected by Blackstead Street. Commerce, executed in glossy Doulton-ware by some sculptor or
sculptors unknown, stands pointing her thumb o'er
her shoulder towards the chimneys of far Hanbridge. When I tell you that the circumference of
that thumb is six inches, and the rest to scale, you
will understand that the statue is one of the prime
glories of Bursley. There were times when Emily
Wrackgarth seemed to herself as vast and as lustrously impressive as it. There were other times
when she seemed to herself as trivial and slavish as
one of those performing fleas she had seen at the
Annual Ladies' Evening Fête organised by the Bursley Mutual Burial Club. Extremist !

She was now stirring the pudding with her left
hand. The ingredients had already been mingled
indistinguishably in that rich, undulating mass of
tawniness which proclaims perfection. But Emily
was determined to give her left hand, not less than
her right, what she called " a doing." Emily was
like that.

At mid-day, when her brother came home from
the Works, she was still at it.

" Brought those scruts with you ? " she asked,
without looking up.

" That's a fact," he said, dipping his hand into
the sagging pocket of his coat.

It is perhaps necessary to explain what scruts are.
In the daily output of every potbank there are a
certain proportion of flawed vessels. These are cast
aside by the foreman, with a lordly gesture, and in

due course are hammered into fragments. These fragments, which are put to various uses, are called scruts ; and one of the uses they are put to is a sentimental one. The dainty and luxurious South-erner looks to find in his Christmas pudding a wed-ding-ring, a gold thimble, a threepenny-bit, or the like. To such fal-lals the Five Towns would say fie. A Christmas pudding in the Five Towns contains nothing but suet, flour, lemon-peel, cinnamon, brandy, almonds, raisins—and two or three scruts. There is a world of poetry, beauty, romance, in scruts—though you have to have been brought up on them to appreciate it. Scruts have passed into the proverbial philosophy of the district. " Him's a pudden with more scruts than raisins to 'm " is a criticism not infrequently heard. It implies respect, even admiration. Of Emily Wrackgarth herself people often said, in reference to her likeness to her father, " Her's a scrut o' th' owd basin."

Jos had emptied out from his pocket on to the table a good three dozen of scruts. Emily laid aside her spoon, rubbed the palms of her hands on the bib of her apron, and proceeded to finger these scruts with the air of a connoisseur, rejecting one after another. The pudding was a small one, designed merely for herself and Jos, with remainder to " the girl " ; so that it could hardly accommodate more than two or three scruts. Emily knew well that one scrut is as good as another. Yet she did not want her brother to feel that anything selected by him would necessarily pass muster with her. For his benefit she ostentatiously wrinkled her nose.

" By the by," said Jos, " you remember Albert Grapp ? I've asked him to step over from Hanbridge and help eat our snack on Christmas Day."

Emily gave Jos one of her looks. " You've asked that Mr. Grapp ? "

" No objection, I hope ? He's not a bad sort. And he's considered a bit of a ladies' man, you know."

She gathered up all the scruts and let them fall in a rattling shower on the exiguous pudding. Two or three fell wide of the basin. These she added :

" Steady on ! " cried Jos. " What's that for ? "

" That's for your guest," replied his sister. " And if you think you're going to palm me off on to him, or on to any other young fellow, you're a fool, Jos Wrackgarth."

The young man protested weakly, but she cut him short.

" Don't think," she said, " I don't know what you've been after, just of late. Cracking up one young sawny and then another on the chance of me marrying him ! I never heard of such goings on. But here I am, and here I'll stay, as sure as my name's Emily Wrackgarth, Jos Wrackgarth ! "

She was the incarnation of the adorably feminine. She was exquisitely vital. She exuded at every pore the pathos of her young undirected force. It is difficult to write calmly about her. For her, in another age, ships would have been launched and cities besieged. But brothers are a race apart, and blind. It is a fact that Jos would have been glad to see his sister " settled "—preferably in one of the other four Towns.

She took up the spoon and stirred vigorously. The scruts grated and squeaked together around the basin, while the pudding feebly wormed its way up among them.

II

Albert Grapp, ladies' man though he was, was humble of heart. Nobody knew this but himself. Not one of his fellow clerks in Clither's Bank knew it. The general theory in Hanbridge was " Him's got a stiff opinion o' hisself." But this arose from what was really a sign of humility in him. He made the most of himself. He had, for instance, a way of his own in the matter of dressing. He always wore a voluminous frock-coat, with a pair of neatly-striped vicuna trousers, which he placed every night under his mattress, thus preserving in perfection the crease down the centre of each. His collar was of the highest, secured in front with an aluminium stud, to which was attached by a patent loop a natty bow of dove-coloured sateen. He had two caps, one of blue serge, the other of shepherd's plaid. These he wore on alternate days. He wore them in a way of his own—well back from his forehead, so as not to hide his hair, and with the peak behind. The peak made a sort of half-moon over the back of his collar. Through a fault of his tailor, there was a yawning gap between the back of his collar and the collar of his coat. Whenever he shook his head, the peak of his cap had the look of a live thing trying to investigate this abyss. Dimly aware of the effect, Albert Grapp shook his head as seldom as possible.

On wet days he wore a mackintosh. This, as he

did not yet possess a great-coat, he wore also, but with less glory, on cold days. He had hoped there might be rain on Christmas morning. But there was no rain. "Like my luck," he said as he came out of his lodgings and turned his steps to that corner of Jubilee Avenue from which the Hanbridge-Bursley trams start every half-hour.

Since Jos Wrackgarth had introduced him to his sister at the Hanbridge Oddfellows' Biennial Hop, when he danced two quadrilles with her, he had seen her but once. He had nodded to her, Five Towns fashion, and she had nodded back at him, but with a look that seemed to say, "You needn't nod next time you see me. I can get along well enough without your nods." A frightening girl! And yet her brother had since told him she seemed "a bit gone, like" on him. Impossible! He, Albert Grapp, make an impression on the brilliant Miss Wrackgarth! Yet she had sent him a verbal invite to spend Christmas in her own home. And the time had come. He was on his way. Incredible that he should arrive! The tram must surely overturn, or be struck by lightning. And yet no! He arrived safely.

The small servant who opened the door gave him another verbal message from Miss Wrackgarth. It was that he must wipe his feet "well" on the mat. In obeying this order he experienced a thrill of satisfaction he could not account for. He must have stood shuffling his boots vigorously for a full minute. This, he told himself, was life. He, Albert Grapp, was alive. And the world was full of other men, all alive; and yet, because they were not doing Miss Wrackgarth's bidding, none of them really lived. He was filled with a vague melancholy. But his melancholy pleased him.

In the parlour he found Jos awaiting him. The table was laid for three.

" So you're here, are you ? " said the host, using the Five Towns formula. " Emily's in the kitchen," he added. " Happen she'll be here directly."

" I hope she's tol-lol-ish ? " asked Albert.

" She is," said Jos. " But don't you go saying that to her. She doesn't care about society airs and graces. You'll make no headway if you aren't blunt."

" Oh, right you are," said Albert, with the air of a man who knew his way about.

A moment later Emily joined them, still wearing her kitchen apron. " So you're here, are you ? " she said, but did not shake hands. The servant had followed her in with the tray, and the next few seconds were occupied in the disposal of the beef and trimmings.

The meal began, Emily carving. The main thought of a man less infatuated than Albert Grapp would have been, " This girl can't cook. And she'll never learn to." The beef, instead of being red and brown, was pink and white. Uneatable beef! And yet he relished it more than anything he had ever tasted. This beef was her own handiwork. Thus it was because she had made it so. . . . He warily refrained from complimenting her, but the idea of a second helping obsessed him.

" Happen I could do with a bit more, like," he said.

Emily hacked off the bit more and jerked it on to the plate he had held out to her.

" Thanks," he said ; and then, as Emily's lip curled, and Jos gave him a warning kick under the table, he tried to look as if he had said nothing.

Only when the second course came on did he suspect that the meal was a calculated protest against his presence. This a Christmas pudding ? The litter of fractured earthenware was hardly held together by the suet and raisins. All his pride of manhood—and there was plenty of pride mixed up with Albert Grapp's humility—dictated a refusal to touch that pudding. Yet he soon found himself touching it, though gingerly, with his spoon and fork.

In the matter of dealing with scruts there are two schools—the old and the new. The old school pushes its head well over its plate and drops the scrut straight from its mouth. The new school emits the scrut into the fingers of its left hand and therewith deposits it on the rim of the plate. Albert noticed that Emily was of the new school. But might she not despise as affectation in him what came natural to herself ? On the other hand, if he showed himself as a prop of the old school, might she not set her face the more stringently against him ? The chances were that whichever course he took would be the wrong one.

It was then that he had an inspiration—an idea of the sort that comes to a man once in his life and finds him, likely as not, unable to put it into practice. Albert was not sure he could consummate this idea of his. He had indisputably fine teeth—" a proper mouthful of grinders " in local phrase. But would they stand the strain he was going to impose on them ? He could but try them. Without a sign of nervousness he raised his spoon, with one scrut in it, to his mouth. This scrut he put between two of his left-side molars, bit hard on it, and—eternity of that moment !—felt it and heard it snap in two. Emily also heard it. He was conscious that at sound of the percussion she started forward and stared at him. But he did not look at her. Calmly, systematically, with gradually diminishing crackles, he reduced that scrut to powder, and washed the powder down with a sip of beer. While he dealt with the second scrut he talked to Jos about the Borough Council's proposal to erect an electric power-station on the site of the old gas-works down Hillport way. He was aware of a slight abrasion inside his left cheek. No matter. He must be more careful. There were six scruts still to be negotiated. He knew that what he was doing was a thing grandiose, unique, epical ; a history-making thing ; a thing that would outlive marble and the gilded monuments of princes. Yet he kept his head. He did not hurry, nor did he dawdle. Scrut by scrut, he ground slowly but he ground exceeding small. And while he did so he talked wisely and well. He passed from the power-station to a first edition of Leconte de Lisle's *Parnasse Contemporain* that he had picked up for sixpence in Liverpool, and thence to the Midland's proposal to drive a tunnel under the Knype Canal so as to link up the main line with the Critchworth and Suddleford loopline. Jos was too amazed to put in a word. Jos sat merely gaping—a gape that merged by imperceptible degrees into a grin. Presently he ceased to watch his guest. He sat watching his sister.

Not once did Albert himself glance in her direc-

tion. She was just a dim silhouette on the outskirts
of his vision. But there she was, unmoving, and
he could feel the fixture of her unseen eyes. The
time was at hand when he would have to meet
those eyes. Would he flinch ? Was he master of
himself ?

The last scrut was powder. No temporising !
He jerked his glass to his mouth. A moment later,
holding out his plate to her, he looked Emily full in
the eyes. They were Emily's eyes, but not hers
alone. They were collective eyes—that was it !
They were the eyes of stark, staring womanhood.
Her face had been dead white, but now suddenly up
from her throat, over her cheeks, through the down
between her eyebrows, went a rush of colour, up
over her temples, through the very parting of her
hair.

" Happen," he said without a quaver in his voice,
" I'll have a bit more, like."

She flung her arms forward on the table and buried
her face in them. It was a gesture wild and meek.
It was the gesture foreseen and yet incredible. It
was recondite, inexplicable, and yet obvious. It
was the only thing to be done—and yet, by gum,
she had done it.

Her brother had risen from his seat and was now at
the door. " Think I'll step round to the Works,"
he said, " and see if they banked up that furnace
aright."

Hilaire Belloc

NEWDIGATE POEM

ON THE BENEFITS OF THE ELECTRIC LIGHT

HAIL, Happy Muse, and touch the tuneful string!
　　The benefits conferred by Science [1] I sing.
　Under the kind Examiners' direction [2]
I only write about them in connection
With benefits which the Electric Light
Confers on us; especially at night.
These are my themes, of these my song shall rise.
My lofty head shall swell to strike the skies.[3]
And tears of hopeless love bedew the maiden's eyes.
　　Descend, O Muse, from thy divine abode,
　　To Osney, on the Seven Bridges Road;
For under Osney's solitary shade
The bulk of the Electric Light is made.
Here are the works;—from hence the current flows
Which (so the Company's prospectus goes)
　Can furnish to Subscribers hour by hour
No less than sixteen thousand candle-power [4]
All at a thousand volts. (It is essential
To keep the current at this high potential
In spite of the considerable expense.)
　The Energy developed represents,
Expressed in foot-tons, the united forces
Of fifteen elephants and forty horses.
But shall my scientific detail thus
Clip the dear wings of Buoyant Pegasus?

---

[1] To be pronounced as a monosyllable in the Imperial fashion.
[2] Mr. Punt, Mr. Howl, and Mr. Grewcock (now, alas, deceased).
[3] A neat rendering of "*Sublimi feriam sidera vertice.*"
[4] To the Examiners: These facts (of which I guarantee the
accuracy) were given me by a Director.

Shall pure statistics jar upon the ear
That pants for Lyric accents loud and clear?
Shall I describe the complex Dynamo
Or write about its Commutator? No!

To happier fields I lead my wanton pen,
The proper study of mankind is men.

Awake, my Muse! Portray the pleasing sight
That meets us when they make Electric Light.

Behold the Electrician where he stands:
Soot, oil, and verdigris are on his hands;
Large spots of grease defile his dirty clothes,
The while his conversation drips with oaths.
Such such a being perish in its youth?
Alas! it is indeed the fatal truth.
In that dull brain, beneath that hair unkempt,
Familiarity has bred contempt.
We warn him of the gesture all too late:
Oh, Heartless Jove! Oh, Adamantine Fate!

A random touch—a hand's imprudent slip—
The Terminals—a flash—a sound like " Zip! "
A smell of burning fills the startled Air—
The Electrician is no longer there!

But let us turn with true artistic scorn
From fates funereal and from views forlorn
Of Erebus and Blackest midnight born!

Arouse thee, Muse! and chaunt in accents rich
The interesting processes by which
The Electricity is passed along:
These are my theme: to these I bend my song.[1]

It runs encased in wood or porous brick
Through copper wires two millimetres thick,
And insulated on their dangerous mission
By indiarubber, silk, or composition.

[1] A reminiscent of Milton " *Fas est et ab hoste docere.* "

Here you may put with critical felicity
The following question : " What is Electricity ? "
  " Molecular Activity," say some,
Others when asked say nothing, and are dumb.
Whatever be its nature, this is clear :
The rapid current checked in its career,
Baulked in its race and halted in its course [1]
Transforms to heat and light its latent force :
  It needs no pedant in the lecturer's chair
To prove that light and heat are present there.
The pear-shaped vacuum globe, I understand,
Is far too hot to fondle with the hand.
While, as is patent to the meanest sight,
The carbon filament is very bright.
As for the lights they hang about the town,
Some praise them highly, others run them down :
This system (technically called the Arc)
Makes some passages too light, others too dark.
  But in the house the soft and constant rays
Have always met with universal praise.
  For instance : if you want to read in bed
No candle burns beside your curtain's head,
For from some distant corner of the room
The incandescent lamp dispels the gloom,
And with the largest print need hardly try
The powers of any young and vigorous eye.
  Aroint thee, Muse ! Inspired the poet sings !
I cannot help observing future things !
Life is a vale, its paths are dark and rough
Only because we do not know enough :

---

[1] Lambkin told me he regretted this line, which was for the
sake of Rhyme. He would willingly have replaced it, but
to his last day could construct no substitute.

When Science has discovered something more
We shall be happier than we were before.
   Hail, Britain, Mistress of the Azure Main,
Ten thousand Fleets sweep over thee in vain !
Hail, Mighty Mother of the Brave and Free,
That beat Napoleon, and gave birth to me !
Thou that canst wrap in thine emblazoned robe
One-quarter of the habitable globe.
Thy mountains, wafted by a favouring breeze,
Like mighty rocks withstand the stormy seas.
   Thou art a Christian Commonwealth ; and yet
Be thou not all unthankful—nor forget,
As thou exultest in Imperial Might,
The Benefits of the Electric Light.

Harry Graham

THE COCKNEY OF THE NORTH
(*W. B. Yeats*)

I WILL arise and go now, and go to Inverness,
   And a small villa rent there, of lath and
     plaster built ;
Nine bedrooms will I have there, and I'll don my
     native dress,
   And walk about in a d—— loud kilt.

And I will have some sport there, when grouse come
     driven slow,
   Driven from purple hill-tops to where the loaders
     quail ;
While midges bite their ankles, and shots are flying
     low,
   And the air is full of the grey-hen's tail.

I will arise and go now, for ever, day and night,
  I hear the taxis bleating and the motor-'buses
    roar,
And over tarred macadam and pavements parched
    and white
  I've walked till my feet are sore !

For it's oh, to be in Scotland ! now that August's
    nearly there,
  Where the capercailzie warble on the mountain's
    rugged brow ;
There's pleasure and contentment, there's sport and
    bracing air,
  In Scotland—now !

Frank Sidgwick

AN ANTIENT POEM

WYNTER ys i-cumen in ;
    Lhoudly syng *tish-u* !
Wyndes blo and snoeth sno,
    And al ys ice nu.
        (Syng *tish-u !*)

Legges trembel after bath,
    And fyngres turneth blu,
Wisker freseth, nosë sneseth—
    Merie syng *tish-u—*
        —tish-u—
        —tish-u—
Wel singest thou *tish-u ;*
Ne stop thou never nu !

THE CHEERFUL CHILTERNS
(*John Masefield*)

OLD man Brown
   Lived near Hampden,
He hated the town
  And often damned en.

Brown had a son
  Who—a boy's habit—
Kept one
  Buck rabbit.

Saturday night
  Home from Wycombe
Brown rolled tight,
  With merry hiccup.

He'd had a wet ;
  Reeling and dribbling
He eyed Tommy's pet,
  A lettuce nibbling.

And being far
  Gone in strong waters,
Laid his cigar
  On the buck's quarters.

It happened so
  In remote Chiltern
Not long ago.
  But worms will turn.

Tommy was angered,
  He could not bear it,
Squared to the drunkard,
  And tapped his claret.

Fury seized Brown,
  Like sparks in tinder,
He knocked Tommy down,
  Kicked the buck outer window.

Tommy took a knife,
  Lay ready for supper,
Let the rich life
  Out of his papa.

Death is so clean,
  Life is so dirty.
Life at eight fifteen,
  Death at eight thirty.

From Brown's lips
  Drooled a curse,
In last eclipse
  He spoke worse
Than ever before.
  " Tom, good-bye.
Death opens a door.
  O grand to die."

And Tommy said,
  " Life is not fair,
I'll soon be dead,
  Dancing on air,

While the horned herds
  Crop the sweet vetches,
And slim brown birds
  Mouse in the hedges."

· · ·

Because he failed
  To curb his knife,
Tom got gaoled
  For life.

Dead now the boy,
  Dead his progenitor.
Life has no joy,
  Death is man's mentor.

Dead the buck rabbit
  In remote Bucks.
Life is so vapid,
  Death reconstructs.

The east wind whistles
  Over the high hill.
Nettles, docks, thistles ;
  Praeterea nihil.

A GRAMMARIAN'S WEDDING
(*Browning*)

[*Note.*—The following lines, recovered from the fly-leaves of a visitors' book at an inn near Florence, appear to form a companion poem to *A Grammarian's Funeral* by Robert Browning, one of whose literary characteristics was a preference for recondite subjects. There would seem to be little doubt that they refer to the story of Speroni Panvinius (as narrated by Bellarmine), who was

born in 1501, and educated at Bologna under the learned
Pomponiatus. He is only less celebrated than his son,
Onuphrius, the historian, possibly the offspring of the union
recorded below, though another story says that Panvinius
was married at least twice.]

L ET us[1] begin to drag our happy pair
    Lapped in their fond ease ;
With blank-verse march our *Io Hymen* share
    Dactyls and spondees.
Not in the streets, for idle fish-eyed gaze,
    Pull we the carriage ;
June shall shed blossoms from her country ways,
    Blessing this marriage.
Sharp to the turn !—we tramp a sweeter gait
    Far from the traffic.
So ! with iambic left-right alternate
    Last of the Sapphic,
Honouring more our Master—he who first
    Scanned the Greek chorus,
Schemed Galliambic, and correctly versed
    Tryphiodorus,
Numbered Lucretius' penthemimerals,
    Ruled his cæsura.
(Strain, biped steeds ! what though the yoke-rope
        galls ?—
    Ilia dura.[2]
Think what's his bee-buzz on her petal lips—
    Epithalamium !—
She silent fragrance to the sound that sips,
    Though but her name he hum !)

[1] The speaker is one of a class of pupils attending the marriage
of their master to a girl-pupil. The poem gives an insight into
an early system of co-education.

[2] An Horatian quotation, which may be translated " Put
your backs into it."

Sweet as the Sea-Born,[1] as Athena wise,
  Glowing as Hebe,
We marked the maid, and said, " Our Master's prize
  Only must she be ! "—
She, the dear promise of an April day
  Slipped from Olympus !
(Hear Laughter-Lover to the Eyes of grey,
  " How mortals imp us ! ")
May fed the hope her June has now fulfilled—
  Sure diagnosis !
Ah, but in May a few of us were thrilled !—
  (That's a *meiosis* [2])—
All ; though no envy where there lay no hope
  Save of disasters ;
Each Jack, too, had his Jill, no misanthrope !—
  She was our Master's.
True, our Bombastes, poor fool, mocked that we
  Brooked such deprival,
Swore, with the valour of the emphatic d——,
  Rout for the rival,
Ambushed our lady, and with all the art
  Wine could provide him
Pleaded, until she from a tender heart
  Gently denied him.
How we then planned, despaired, hoped, plotted,
      guessed,
  Wondered, conjectured !
Fire in her eyes alone of all the rest
  Watched him who lectured ;
Not till he met it could her brave gaze shift,
  Δῖα γυναικῶν ! [3]

---

[1] Aphrodite or Venus. So " Laughter-Lover " below.
[2] An under-statement.
[3] " God-like among women "—an Homeric phrase.

Our sappy pines on winter hearths burn swift ;
 Swifter the dry cone.

Poring on scholiast script with single eye,
 Poor Polyphemus !

Nursing a goddess—we, the common fry—
 How should he deem us ?

What else drove blood in wizened cheek again,
 Gave him his two eyes ?

We pushed a Galatea [1] in his ken,
 Her and her blue eyes !

Hopes lit him ; questioned qualms " If Love should
 cheat ? "
 (How the days wore on !)

Age posed his bitter 'gainst her springing sweet ;
 " There's *oxymoron* ! [2]

Aye, and the oil and water in one flask ?—
 Æschylus hints it." [3]

What's Nature or her laws ? That's Love's own
 task ;
 Omnia vincit ! [4]

Omnia vicit, too ! (What coward jeers
 " Atropos occat " ? [5]

On *this* day speak of the abhorred shears ?
 What's here to mock at ?

---

[1] Galatea was a maid with whom, according to Theocritus,
Polyphemus fell in love.

[2] A classical figure, signifying the collocation of opposites.

[3] Cf. *Agamemnon*, 322. Æschylus actually says " *vinegar*
and oil " ; but the result is the same.

[4] " Omnia vincit amor," " Love conquers all " ; from Vergil's
Eclogues. The change of tense in the next line implies " Love
conquered all," in this case.

[5] Part of a Latin hexameter, meaning that, of the Three
Fates, Clotho held the distaff, Lachesis span, and Atropos
cut the thread. The anticipation of Milton, *Lycidas* 75, is
interesting.

" Mori memento," quoth Bombastes ; hark
  Knell to the nuptial !—
Roll hounds i' th' ditch ! to-day no dog shall bark,
  No, nor a pup shall !)
Here's the wreathed cottage, fit for them alone.
  Peace to our shoving !
Our part is done ; the rest is all their own,
  Living and loving.
Over the threshold lift his laughing bride—
  Don't let it trip her !
Shut the door . . .
    H'mph ! it's autumn now outside.
  There ! the last slipper !

E. V. Knox

REDFORD, MUSAGELIS[1]
(*Matthew Arnold*)

NOT here, my good fellow,
 Are plays meet for you,
But where Aldwych is hoisting
 Its pomp to the blue ;

Or where moon-smitten millions
 Unceasingly crowd
At the entrance of Daly's—
 Go there and be proud.

To the seats on the house-top
 The multitude flock ;
They are fighting their hunger
 With peppermint rock.

[1] Mr. Redford was Censor of Plays.

On the *fauteuil* beneath sits
  The blue-blooded swell ;
He has robed him and dined him
  Remarkably well.

What gowns are these coming ?
  What hats, and by whom ?
What skirt-trains outsweeping
  The vacuum broom ?

What sweet-breathing music
  Unchastened by Time ?
What hosen illumed by
  The light of the lime ?

'Tis EDWARDS presenting
  His loveliest dream !
They all were stupendous,
  But this is the cream !

Lo, here is the drama
  Your wits understand ;
The Muse you have fostered
  And foist on our land !

The choruses chirrup
  And pass to the wings ;
The wags entertain us
  And somebody sings.

What strife do they tell of ?
  What passions expound ?
Why, earth and the motive
  That makes her go round.

First show they the flirting
   Of flappers and then
The rest of existence
   The childhood of men ;

The dance in its daring,
   The Corybant's wreath ;
The time-honoured chestnut
   The Stars and their teeth.

UPON JULIA'S CLOTHES

(*Herrick*)

WHENAS in furs my Julia goes,
   Of slaughtered vermin goodness
knows,
What tails depend upon her clothes !

Next, when I cast my eyes and see
The living whelp she lugs to tea,
Oh, how their likeness taketh me !

THE STEAM-GIVERS

(*Alfred Noyes*)

PART I

AUSTERE, remote, immeasurably proud
   And filled with shining levers that control
The health and happiness of half the world
The signal cabin at East Croydon Main
Beckoned me upwards.

                    For the signalman
Had said, " To-morrow, if you care to see
The way the London, Brighton and South Coast
Directs her passing traffic, you may come " ;
And I said, " Right-o."

                    When I went upstairs
I found a calmness. More significant
That calm than all the busy toil below ;
That calm than all the shrieking of the trains
That strove to rend it. Dominant, serene,
That signal box with all its telephones,
The train and sinews of a host of arms,
Prophetically reared or dropped to rest,
The sun and centre of a host of stars
That shimmer through the darkness of our night :
Sole guide to all those intermingling threads
Of silvern rivers running to the sea,
Of main and branch lines bounded by the sea,
Fraught with innumerable ballast trains,
And steering onward to predestined ends
Express and ordinary passengers—
There in that box I found a windless calm.
I saw the needles pointing to " Line clear,"
" Train out of section," or to " Train on line " ;
I heard the bells beat, many different bells
Beating with different tones for " up " and " down ",
With different pauses in between the bells
For different trains, carrying cattle and men,
Fruit, meat and milk and perishable goods,
Breakdowns and empties.

                    I observed the clocks
And all the various gadgets everywhere

Connected with the interlocking frame,
The levers, red and white and black and green,
And tried to understand the lock and block
System itself ; but I was foiled by that.
Aye ! lock and block, ye were too much for me !
But as I tried I seemed to hear a voice,
A voice between the tinklings of the bells,
That said, " We were the fathers " ; seemed to see
Shadows of those great spirits of the past,
Silent discoverers, lonely pioneers ;
And first of all that one who, handing on
The spark of fire from the immense profound,
Improved the stationary steam engine
And made it fit for locomotive use.

He was a great mechanic, was James Watt,
Of lowland stock, too weakly as a child
For regular attendances at school,
So that quite often, when the school-bell splashed
The air with sound, he stayed beside the fire.
Much from his mother's teaching he would learn,
Much from his father's ; but still more he taught
Himself unaided.

           At nineteen his love
For making mathematic instruments
Lured him to London. But, returning thence
To Glasgow, Glasgow proved unkind to him,
His more than common capabilities
Provoking strange hostility among
The Incorporated Guild of Hammermen ;
Till wiser souls than theirs, more apt to see
How light leaps forth from learning, knowledge
    springs

Ever from seeking knowledge, not routine,
Helped the ingenious James and found him an
Appointment at the University.

He was a great mechanic, was James Watt.
And whether now, as some would have it first,
Or earlier in the cottage where he toiled
Beside the firelight, and one day at tea,
Seeing the kettle's lifted lid (such power
The boiling water had to heave the thing
Upward), he turned his adolescent mind
To muse upon the motive strength of steam—
Thus much is sure, that, always murmuring "Steam",
And "Steam, more steam", he hit as in a flash
One day on that sublime experiment,
The separate condenser, which o'ercame
The loss of steam inside the cylinder.

He was a great mechanic, was James Watt.
And ever as he toiled and murmured "Steam"
He sang some stave to wile the weary hours
And break the page, some little stave like this—

In old Cathay, in far Cathay
    Before the West espied the gleam,
Philosophers had found no way
    Of fruitfully condensing steam.
With instruments that went by hand
    Their unenlightened path they trod ;
The Chinese did not understand
    The uses of the piston-rod.

On camel-back from Araby
    Transporting frankincense and myrrh,

The old Arabians failed to see
   Much object in a cylinder;
But where is Araby by now?
   She fades away and is forgot,
While all the world remembers how
   The steam-engine was built by Watt.

The lion wanders round at nights
   Where Jamshid made a marble tower
According to his simple lights
   With merely manual motive power;
Dishonoured now is Jamshid laid
   In desert courts where once he drank;
He might have done far more for trade
   By using my ingenious crank.

In Babylon, in Babylon,
   They frittered half their time away
With futile variations on
   Contrivances that did not pay;
For Belus' sake they built a shrine,
   But Belus now is dead and gone;
And fly-wheels much resembling mine
   Will soon be used in Babylon.

So singing always as he laboured on,
Watt worked at engines, till at last his life
Drew to a tranquil and an honoured close
At Heathfield, fairly near to Birmingham.
And though they say he never would consent
To smile upon the tractive use of steam,
And even put a clause into his lease

That no steam carriage should approach his house,
Yet paved the path for Stephenson to build
The earliest locomotive.

　　　　　　　　　　　　So he died.
He was a great mechanic, was James Watt.

PART II

" Steam and more steam ! " The spark from
　　heaven was there !
The separate condenser made by Watt
Was followed by Trevithick's steam-engine.
Train-roads existed. Now the golden dawn.

George Stephenson, whom half Great Britain knew
As " Geordie ", since the day that flashed his fame
Above the stars, that day of contests on
The line from Liverpool to Manchester,
Dreamily watched his wife, Elizabeth,
Setting the tea-things for their simple tea,
To which the poet Wordsworth had been asked,
And was expected to arrive at four ;
For " Certainly, dear friends," he said, " I'll come ;
Science advances with gigantic strides,
And I shall be extremely glad to meet
The maker of ' The Rocket '."

　　　　　　　　　　　　On the sill
A robin hopped. The old cat Sawney mewed.
Now the March sunlight, streaming through the
　　room
To gild the teapot spout, was suddenly dimmed.
A shadow crossed the window. Wordsworth came.

" How are you, Geordie ? "   One swift clasp of
   hands,
And " William, hoo's yersen ? "

                  They talked awhile
Of buds and birds, and how the English spring
Enhances the idyllic scenery
Of Grasmere, Buttermere and Rydal Head.
Then Wordsworth : " Tell me all the story now
By what vast pains ' The Rocket ' came to be " ;
And Stephenson, half-bashful and half-proud,
Finished his slice of tea-cake and began,
Not as I tell it, Englished, but more slow,
In the rude Doric of his Northern tongue ;
While, gazing on her man with glimmering eyes,
Mirrors of his new fame, Elizabeth
Hung on his words and half forgot the tea.

" Despite ' The Puffing Billy ' patented
In eighteen hundred and thirteen, there still
Remained some faults, some standing faults, in all
The earlier types of engine.   Our steam-power
Not yet was adequate or uniform.
Device upon device was still employed
To raise the necessary furnace draught.
So, musing on these things, at last I said,
' Aye, but the waste steam could be utilized
To stimulate combustion by a draught.'
Hence sprang ' The Rocket ', and the rest you
   know."

" At Rainhill, I believe," the poet said,
" She hauled a coach with thirty passengers

Along the stated course, and at the speed
Of thirty miles an hour." "Aye, that she
    did,"
Said Stephenson, " and so I won the prize—
Five hundred pounds, a prize not small to win ;
And having won it, made a little song,
Part mine and partly borrowed from your own
About ' The Rocket '. May I sing it, sir ? "
" You may," said Wordsworth. Then in rhythmic
    tones,
Beating the table with a spoon, he sang—

" THE TRIUMPH OF STEAM "

" Oh, think not aught shall bar the way ;
The steam engine has come to stay.
The crags and dales, the fretful burns
Shall soon be bridged by these concerns,
And puffs of smoke on hill-sides proud
Shall wander lonely as a cloud.

" Through larch and oak and beech and pine
You shall behold that glory shine,
And think how many an inland home
Grows hourly nearer to the foam,
Till all your heart with gladness fills
And dances like the railway bills.

" As silver strands of cobweb drawn
Across the grass at early dawn
The lines shall fill all England, sir,
With their industrial gossamer,
Facilitating as they run
Our trade communication.

" ' The Rocket ' soars into the skies ;
With all our hopes and fears she flies
With beef and coal, with beer and blocks
Of ordinary shares and stocks ;
We set no limit to our dream
Till all the dales shall pant with steam,
And puffs of smoke on hill-sides proud
Shall wander lonely as a cloud."

Thus murmuring with rhythmic beat and slow,
And tapping on the table, Stephenson
Had sunk his head awhile upon his breast.
Now he looked up. But Wordsworth was not
    there.
The Bard of Rydal had removed himself.
Annoyed ? Maybe. Yet Stephenson was right.
For we who, gazing on " The Rocket " now,
Think to ourselves how rummy it appears
With its long funnel and peculiar wheels
Ought to remember that the changes made
Since 1830 in the size and shape
Of locomotive engines have been more
Matters of detail than of principle.

THE LAST BUS

(*W. de la Mare*)

NID-NOD through shuttered streets at dead of
    night
  Soundless the last grey motor-bus went home ;
Hailed it no watcher in its phantasm flight ;
  Up the steep belfry stair no passenger clomb.

Mute as a mammet, bowed above the wheel
  The driver.   His moustache was green with moss
Cobwebs about him had begun to steal ;
  Deafer than dammit the conductor was.

Red rust was on the gear chain.   Hung long trails
  Of bugloss and bindweed from the bonnet's crown ;
Charlock and darnel cluttered up the rails ;
  The destination boards were upside down.

Yet still the bus moved, billowy with grass,
  Tottered and laboured, spurted, swayed and
      slowed ;
Stock still the constable beheld it pass ;
  Bunched sat the cat and feared to whisk the road.

Doom-loud the vegetable transport train
  Thundered their hallos, ground the earth to grit ;
Scavengers turned to wave and wave again,
  Night revellers screamed " Toot-a-loot " to it.

And still no sound.   Only a murmur, a sigh
  Showed it not all a thing of shadow and gleam ;
Fled the tall soap-works, fled the brewery by,
  Fled the municipal baths as though in a dream.

None knew whence came this shadowy motor-bus,
  What it was doing, why, and whither away
It sped on into the night adventurous,
  Covered with lichens and all a-shake with hay.

Aye, but the forms within !   What face was that
  Glassily seen—and that one, mild yet mum ?
There—with the pink petunia in her hat !
  There—with the purple pelargonium !

And some have parcels of meat and fish and tea,
  And some eat aniseed from paper bags,
And some with sightless eyes scan momently
  Novels—yet turn no page—and fictional mags.

Fares are not asked. Time here is all withdrawn ;
  A tenderness is here most tranquil and sweet ;
As the still bus incessantly sails on
  Nobody stamps on anybody's feet.

Till see ! They are out beyond the shuttered streets,
  Beyond the edge of the pavement and the trams.
A wonderful change ! The ghosts stir in their seats.
  Dawn glints. The first grey light shows fields of
    lambs.

Lollops a coney ; peeps from tangled hedge
  Bright eye of weasel (so unvexed the route) ;
Sits tit and sways on perilous blossom's edge ;
Squabbles a squirrel ; ululates a coot.

Bluebells start up, fantastically long,
  Cowslip and cuckoo pint ; all round the wheels
Dactyls wave arms and extra syllables throng
  Looping the felloes. Topples the bus and heels.

And now an amazing sense of freedom from care
  Deliciously moves their hearts as out they get.
This is the terminus. Rose-sweet the air,
  Although underfoot the ground is still quite wet.

Leaves his sad perch the driver. Laughing and gay,
  Lands the conductor a friendly slap on the snout ;
They bind the engine anew with a twist of hay ;
  All breathe, dance, skip, take breakfast, scamper
    about.

THE CIGARETTE GATHERER

(*E. B.*)

NOW all the lispering runnels are dried up
    That swilled the orts and refuse in time of
        rain ;
Down the hutched gateway hollowed like a cup,
    Match-sticks strew gutters and chaff cheats the
        drain.

The dog-day sun now pitilessly glares,
    Street-lightning flickers from crossed rails of
        trams.
Puffs powder noses. Newsboys bleat their wares.
    Shrill as to browsing yoes baa food-foiled lambs.

Stewed asphalt softens. Barrow-trundlers ply
    Good trade for scoop of tongues from horn twist
        roll ;
Butchers beat off the blackening thunder-fly
    From meat ; in houses gas replaces coal.

But out in that dry gutter sloven and bent
    The old fag-gleaner still goes channering on
With pale blotched face and in his hat a dent
    And coat green-slimed as sluice when mill-flood's
        gone.

Holding an elmen stick in knarréd hands
    He mucks and mouches, prodding here and there
'Mongst pips and paper, heedless of what brands
    The found stumps be ; to him they all are
        fair.

MYSTERY

(*Joseph Conrad*)

I HADN'T seen Burleigh for some five years or more when I found him waiting for me that fine light evening in the long low-roofed room with the red curtains—all sailormen know it—at the back of "The Ebb Tide." The front rooms of the tavern of course look out on the square grey shipping offices of the Ultramarine Company, just where the tramway forks—I never could make out, by the way, where that tramway goes to—but Robinson keeps this upstairs room with the bay-windows, the one that looks out over the docks, for a few favoured customers, amongst whom I am privileged to count myself.

Robinson didn't seem to have altered much, I thought. The same white puffed-out cheeks like an elderly cherub in need of fresh air, and the thick black eyebrows that seemed to wave and rustle as if in some invisible wind. Mrs. Robinson was much the same too—angular, moving obscurely in the background, with those thin lips and that faint everlasting smile.

The first part of Burleigh that I noticed when I went upstairs and opened the door was his broad back, encased as usual in a frock-coat of No. 1 sailcloth, the tails of which fell slightly apart as he bent downwards to light his pipe at the fire with a long twist of old newspaper. When he stood up and turned round I was relieved to see that he had not altered either. The ring of fine curly hair that ran round the crown of his otherwise bald head was thinner than it had been, but there was the same lugubrious drollery in his grey eyes and the same gentle murmuring voice that came so incongruously from his deep stalwart chest as though through a sort of syrup. He had that old trick too of his of smiling so that one end of his mouth ran up suddenly against the barrier of his heavy moustache, like the curl of a wave on a spit of reef. The large white-cotton umbrella, badly rolled up, that he always carried when ashore, was still hanging by its crook from his huge right arm.

" Have a——" he said quizzically, and I signified assent in the usual manner. As we sat down at the gleaming mahogany table and looked at each other smiling across it, he knew, of course—how could he help knowing?—that I wanted to hear all about that remarkable cruise of the " Albatross " away in the Southern ice floes about which the whole water-side was talking and about which nobody surely was likely to know more than he did. But equally of course he wasn't going to tell me all at once, for that wasn't Burleigh's way. Instead he tugged dreamily at one of his big moustaches and smiled up into the end of the other as we looked out at the lighted tideway beneath. Lamps shone high, shone low there, shone with single eyes, shone in rows, were reflected in glittering ladders broken by the shadows of hawsers along the oily inquietude of the stream. Congregated and at rest, the ships seemed to cast gentle inquiring glances at one another, to ask how each had fared in the vast incalculable tangle of wet mysteriousness which passes under the name of the sea.

Burleigh gave a final tug at last and spoke.

" I've asked another man in here to-night to meet you in a kind of way," he said with a sort of depreciatory wave of his big hand as though it was a species of liberty to ask one man to meet another. And then, clearing his throat and twisting his smile again—" Man called Allotson, Jim Allotson " ; and, as if with a sudden effort of memory and dragging the words up from some deep recess of his vast interior—" second mate."

" Not on the——" I began, but he stopped me at once with the heavy emphatic nod characteristic of him.

" First man up the berg-side," he cooed in that surprisingly gentle voice. " Girl on it. Sicilian dancer, I believe. Derelict. Polar bears too. Good man, Jim Allotson. I'll tell you about him before he comes."

And bit by bit I came to piece out, between the nods of Burleigh's head and the tuggings of that moustache of his and his quick sideways smile, the history of Allotson's youth up to the day when, by one of those extraordinary coincidences that sailors call chance, he became second officer of the " Albatross "—became second officer and so had his share of the tragi-comedy that was to happen to the crew of about the most adventurous tramp that was ever beaten out of the trade routes into the frozen seas.

He had been the son of a rather superior ship's chandler, I gathered, of a pious disposition, who settled down in East Croydon of all places after retiring from the sight and smell of salt water as they came to him on the quay-side at Singapore. Neither a gravel subsoil nor excessive church-going

was able to ward off malaria for long. He soon
went under—his wife had died some years before—
and left the child to the care of his only surviving
relative, a sister named Ann. I can see her now
as Burleigh described her to me, with her tight
lips, expressionless eyes, grey coils of hair and the
black alpaca dress she always inhabited, checking,
reproving, forbidding and instilling endless moral
axioms into this touzle-headed waif who had the
rover's blood so inalienably in his veins.

He ran away, of course. He was bound to run
away, had always dreamed and thought of nothing
but ropes and rigging and tar, had seen the alley-
ways of his snug suburban home as tidal inlets
hung with tropical vegetation ; ran away and got
a berth as ship's boy, and at fifteen had seen as
much of the strange places of the world as many
of us achieve in a life-time. He had frizzled in
pestilential mud-flats, been driven under storm-
sails by the stark spite of typhoons, opened up
hidden creeks, the passionless offshoots of unknown
estuaries, at a time when other lads were grinding
away at their Rule of Three.

Somehow or other, Burleigh did not exactly know
how, he had managed to get his second-mate's
certificate. But what he did know was that all
through those wanderings the young man had
preserved a sort of simple charming piety that
came perhaps from the early lessons of that vigorous
uncompromising old lady in Croydon, intolerable
though her maxims had seemed.

" Good man, Jim Allotson," cooed Burleigh once
more at the end of all this, as though it were a
kind of refrain. And just then the door opened

and a man came in. He was dressed in a blue
reefer suit, stooped slightly and walked a little
lame. So much I saw as I gradually drew my eyes
upward from the bright spot of light at the bottom
of Burleigh's grog glass, where they had been fixed
with a sort of fascination while he spoke. Raised
now to the level of the stranger's own, they blinked
a little, and I held my breath for a moment at the
contrast between that fresh ruddy face with slight
black whiskers and the crop of hair that surmounted
it, white as a bank of snow. He had the grey
eyes that seem to be searching out the eternal
riddle of heaven and sea, even when they have no
further to look than the end of a room. Down
the left cheek ran a broad whitey-brown scar that
shocked almost as though it were unnatural and
had been painted on. I did not need Burleigh's
purred introduction to the second mate of the
" Albatross " to have my curiosity, already pretty
lively, as you know, whipped up to fever-point ;
and my friend's, " This young man is very anxious
to hear——" could have been read without trouble
in my eyes.

" But how much have you told him already ? "
he asked, speaking with a slight stammer as he
raised his glass and held it out a little stiffly in
front of him, as though this was a necessary pre-
liminary before putting it to his lips. I found out
later that this was an invariable trick of his. " Have
you told him how I got my second-mate's certificate ? "

Burleigh shook his head. He didn't, of course,
as I was aware, know.

" About fourteen years ago," began Allotson,

and I sighed a little ; but before he had said another word the door opened again.

There was something horribly uncanny about that opening of the door, not followed by the appearance of a body but only of a face, as if it had been cut off at the neck——

" Time, gentlemen, please," said the voice of Robinson.

THE PECULIAR BIRD

(*H. G. Wells*)

" 'ENG ! " said Mr. Bottleby, addressing the eighteenth milestone with intense bitterness : " 'Eng ! "

The bright windy sunshine on that open downland road, the sense of healthy effort, of rhythmic trundling speed, the consciousness of the nearly new ready-to-wear gent's cycling costume which draped his limbs—it had been ticketed " ENORMOUS REDUCTION," and, underneath that again, " STARTLING SACRIFICE, 25/6 ", in Parkinson's great front window on the South Parade—none of these things had availed to dissipate the gradual gloom which had been settling like a miasma on Mr. Bottleby's mind through the whole of that morning of May. Various causes, historical, social as well as physiological, had contributed their share towards that tenebrous exhalation which already seemed to hang about him like a tangible and visible cloud. But undoubtedly its immediate origin and the cause of his hasty flight was the state of the Break-

fast Bacon. Greasy. Uneatable. Tck! How
many times had he told Ann, a hundred times if
he had told her once, that he liked it in little crisp
hard pieces and the eggs poached separately on
toast? He was Fed Up. That was it. Abso-
bloominglutely Fed. Tck!

If some well-meaning social philosopher had
attempted to explain to Mr. Bottleby the exact
processes whereby a wasteful and ill-organized
civilization had condemned him to struggle Laocoon-
like in the coils of the retail ironmongery and the
embraces of an uncongenial spouse, it is doubtful
whether Mr. Bottleby would have clearly understood. But his resentment against fate was none
the less profound because it was largely inarticulate
and because he would probably have summed up
all this mismanagement and stupidity and care-
lessness and insensate cruelty in some simple
epigram like " A bit too thick." Vaguely, in the
recesses of his being, Mr. Bottleby knew that in
some way or other there ought to have been for
him a more beautiful and gracious existence, a life
somehow different from the drudgery and pettiness
that he endured. . . .

The shop . . . How he hated it! How he did
hate it! Ironmongery! Fast bound—What was
it they had said in that church he had strayed
into one evening? Misery and iron? Yes, that
was it. Fast bound in misery and iron. That
was him. And Ann. Sometimes when he thought
of Ann . . . Skinny. Complaining. And why
the doose did she cook like that? . . . There
were other things too. In fact, there was One
Thing after Another.

" 'Eng ! " repeated Mr. Bottleby to the nine-teenth milestone ; " 'Eng " !

And having come now to the rather precipitous winding lane which leads down into Fittlehurst village he placed his feet on the rests—it was long before the luxurious days of the free-wheel—folded his arms and began to coast. Perilously, but with a certain sense of satisfaction in his extreme reck-lessness, to coast. . . .

One figures him, a slightly rotund shape of about three-and-thirty years of age, attired in the check knickerbocker suit which had meant such an earth-shaking sacrifice to Mr. Parkinson ; one figures him, I say, with his freckled face, pleasant brown eyes and that large tuft of hair which continually escaped the control of his cap peak, rushing rapidly, worried, tormented by destiny, between those tall hedges on which the hawthorn had already made patches of scented, almost delirious, bloom, rushing downwards—on. . . .

Whuck !

I come now upon a difficulty. I find it exceed-ingly hard to describe to you the nature of that surprising existence to which Mr. Bottleby awoke when, having caught the fallen telegraph wire—fallen in yesterday's gale so that it blocked the Fittlehurst road like a piece of paddock fencing—having caught this wire exactly under his chin, he was projected out and away into the Ultimate Beyond.

His first impression was agreeable enough. It was one of amazing lightness. And, looking down with those pleasant brown eyes of his, he found that there was indeed good reason for this. For all that lower corporeal part of Mr. Bottleby, that envelope of complicated tubes and piping which had been the source of so much of his trouble, that foundation for the altruistic sartorial efforts of Mr. Parkinson, had completely disappeared. The bicycling suit, and all that therein was, had ceased to be. It had been even more Greatly Reduced. It had been Sacrificed Entirely. And simultaneously Mr. Bottleby was conscious of a kind of soft and feathery growth to right and left of him, a faint iridescent fluffiness a little way behind each of his ears. At the same moment he also became conscious of the fact that he was not alone. All about him, floating, if I may so put it, though the phrase is a singularly inapt one, were thousands of similarly bodiless beings with bright and tiny wings attached to their necks. There was a sound, too, as of a mighty chattering. All these beings were talking, talking hard, talking with a shrill pleasant chirrup like that of song-birds at dawn.

" Queer go," muttered Mr. Bottleby. " Sort of cherribim. Tck."

And instantly he found himself twittering too.

But around and over and under and interpenetrating these more immediate impressions of his a tremendous alteration had come over the mentality of Mr. Bottleby, an alteration that I almost despair of making intelligible. For he was now Out of Time and Out of Space. He was conscious of the Eternal, of the Infinite. The universe as a concrete fact and the universe as a process of change were for him merged into one. The barriers separating history, biology, astronomy, were broken down.

I can perhaps give a faint hint of that new strange

consciousness of his when I say that a simultaneous and precisely equivalent impact was now being made on Mr. Bottleby's optical retinæ by the emergency of a huge plesiosaurus from a bog of slime, the murder of JULIUS CÆSAR, and the efforts of a morose and scowling Ann to remove the remnants of bacon grease from a broken willow-pattern plate.

There was also the Future. . . .

One would have thought that this expansion of vision, this sudden opening, as it were, of a thousand intellectual flood-gates, would have suffused Mr. Bottleby's brain with a sense of ineffable beatitude. But it was not so. Whether it was because he was not really fitted for so rapid a translation from the terrestrial to the supernal environment —he was, as a matter of fact, still wearing his bicycling cap,—I cannot say ; but the fact remains that in the secret places of his ego Mr. Bottleby was bored, abominably bored. And quite soon, if I may use this inaccurate temporal expression, he made up his mind that, if it were possible, he would abscond.

" Vamoose," he twittered. " Clear. Get out of it."

Curiously enough, he found that he could. By holding his breath very hard till both cheeks and eyes bulged, he found that the infinite consciousness began mysteriously to recede, whilst the terrestrial in some peculiar way enhanced itself. The winged head of Mr. Bottleby began to sink ; I should rather say to emerge. Infinity, like a slow sunset, like the memory of a dream, faded. Speaking again in temporal phraseology, Mr. Bottleby became a sort of meteorite, a flying fragment, a detached chip of immortality.

.　　　.　　　.　　　.

The question of who was really the first to see the Strange Bird is still hotly debated in the bar parlour of " The Blue Pig " at Fittlehurst. It was certainly seen at ten o'clock by the young man who was dressing the window of Hipley the haberdasher, because his testimony is confirmed by that of the Doctor, who saw it at the same time and said so afterwards to the Vicar. And undoubtedly at half-past ten or thereabouts it perched on one of the great branches of the village oak, for two small boys saw it there and threw stones at it. Equally certain that just before noon it was seen making for the gap in the downs by old Marley the hedger.

" Girt bumblesome thing," he reports it to have been. And then, scratching his head, " Sure-ly."

In any case it was a chance visitor to Pipley-on-Sea, a man named Herringshaw, who wantonly fired at it from the sands near the big breakwater by the bathing-huts at 2.45 p.m. and winged it. Flopping heavily and cumbrously, it dipped down to the waves, rose unsteadily, flopped back and was seen for some time tossing from sunlit crest to crest before it passed out with the tide. It was never heard of again.

Nobody thought of connecting it with the headless body of Mr. Bottleby, the retail ironmonger, which was found entangled with his wrecked bicycle two-thirds of the way down Fittlehurst lane.

S. Baghot de la Bere
THE WAY HOME
(*H. Belloc*)

IT was seven o'clock in the evening when I had finished sitting in the " Hippogrif " at Armentières. I had been drinking that black strong wine they sell there that is called Hardigras, but in Cahors and round about St. Cirq, and the valley of the Lôt, *Coup de Ventre* ; and they do well who call it so, for indeed it is a very noble wine and well suited to the stomachs of Catholic men.

And while I was drinking it I sang that song that the Venerable Sanchia Sangruelle sang to Piers Vidoq when he was tempted of the devil, as is fully set out in the Life of the Abbot of Dax to the greater glory of God and the everlasting confusion of heretics.

Now when I had made an end of singing I thought me of the South Country where I live and which Heaven and St. Cuthlac have otherwise blessed in many and singular ways. So I called for more drink for me and my friends, who were sitting by the wall, and when we had drunk it I said :

" I will go to my own country."

And one, who was strongly wrapped about with haybands and drank his wine apart from the rest, sitting under the dresser of chestnut wood after the custom of the men from Tours l'Asile, said : " It is good for a man to be in his own country : for there indeed he may sing over his liquor the songs of his own people, who may (with the help of the saints) even have pleasure in them."

And as he said this all that good company who

were sitting in the inn beat upon the board with their mugs and cried " Ochlier, Ochlier ! " that is to say, " We agree." So I went and sat by the man from Tours l'Asile, for it seemed to me that we should agree well together, and I was minded to tell him the story of Og the Eremite and Patapan, the Burgrave of Silesia.

But it so chanced that, before I had made an end of telling, the sun had slanted down behind the poplar-trees in the valley beyond Carcasonne, and the company had gone away to their homes, and the man from Tours l'Asile took down his sickle from the wall and said in a strong voice, " Comprend pas," which is a phrase they use in those parts (and even so far to the south as Pontaven and the country of the accursed Patarines), and is as much as to say : " I have no idea what you are talking about."

And having by this time drunk out his liquor, he would stay no longer with me at the inn, but spat upon the ground and went away to his home after the heathenish fashion of the men from his village who have no good-fellowship in them since the Prior of Arles laid them under the Greater Excommunication for the singing of lewd songs and putting nutmeg in their hot-cross buns, which things they do to this day.

These and other matters I turned over in my mind as I set out, and, walking strongly, came at dawn to the little hill called Bec d'Or, which has a grove of oak-trees, where I had a mind to breakfast off some bread and garlic which I carried in my pocket, and a quart of ale which I had bought from a poor man in Armentières.

This I hold to be the best breakfast for a man in a country other than his own, that is to say, Sussex—or rather those parts of it which lie about Little Piddinghoe and to the west of Brede. For those lands which lie farther to the north did not get the faith until after Gudrac the Goole divided the land, and retain to this day many swinish and besotted customs.

Now, as I sat eating my breakfast and watching the sun rise behind the forty-seven spires of Narbonne, I determined to compose a song in honour of St. Basil the Patriarch, who came to live here after the heathen had sacked Alexandria, and to set it to a very good tune I had learnt from a man who sold cat's-meat in Ghisle.

But, first, I made a map of the place and put dragons in it and unicorns and a mermaid and the points of the compass, so that men might know the place and come there when I am lying in my grave by the Rother with my head to the weald and my feet to the sea.

Now the song that I made was as follows :—

THE SONG OF THE SEVEN KINGS

King Herod the Tetrarch had cellars of wine,
And he fed his ha*reem* on the flesh of the swine,
He buttoned his breeches and buckled his shoes
And sent forth his legions to worry the Jews.
He swore at his wife in most scandalous terms,
And he laughed at the Pope and the Diet of Worms.

Chorus

Hic, haec, he buckled his shoe,
He swore at his wife when he'd nothing to do,
Clamavit in Poculis hullabaloo.

When I had sung this over a few times and drunk some more ale I made a second verse :

King Pepin the Pious he reigned in Gisors.
He had seven-and-thirty confessors or more.
He wore a hair shirt every day of his life
And refused to cohabit with Brenda his wife.
He wielded the scourge till his shoulders were raw,
And he pawned the Crown Jewels to sleep in the straw.

Chorus

Eheu, Eheu, what more could he do ?
He beat himself black and he banged himself blue,
Misericordia hullabaloo.

Now the rest of this song will be found written down in its proper place, for I must tell now of the adventure of

THE THREE MURDERERS OF ST. POL

whom (at this moment) I saw coming between the trees, bearing with them a hideous creature in a fur coat with a kind of mask about the upper part of his face. I had a sort of terror at the sight of this horrid ruffian, who had all the appearance of a very rich and wicked man ; but, seeing that he was bound with cords and that those who held him were very strong resolute men, I went down to meet them and to offer them what was left of the ale, for they were weary with dragging the fat hideous man in his heavy coat.

MYSELF (*offering the jar of ale*) : " Can I be of any assistance to you gentlemen murderers ? "

FIRST MURDERER (*taking off his hat*) : " We are obliged to you, sir. Have you by chance such a thing as a rope ? "

MYSELF : " No."

SECOND MURDERER (*peevishly*) : " I told you so, Gil. This worthy gentleman has no rope."

MYSELF (*sitting down upon a fallen tree*) : " Perhaps you will tell me if I can serve you otherwise, and why you drag this hideous fat man with you ? "

THIRD MURDERER : " But very willingly, sir. We found this man on the road where we were walking peacefully. He was lying under a kind of machine that made a snorting noise while he beat upon its belly with a piece of iron. So upon the advice of Gustave here, to whom he is well known, we drew him from under the machine and brought him here that we might hang him from a tree. For you cannot imagine the evil that this man has wrought throughout the country."

Now this made me the more curious to learn the trade or calling of the fat hideous man, for at first I had thought that he might be a manufacturer of cocoa or one of those obscene and filthy creatures, exponents of the Higher Criticism who eat no flesh meat and read the novels of Gogol and Turgeniev. But the courteous murderers assured me that it was not so ; neither (for all his great wealth) was he a Promoter of Companies nor an actor for the Movies nor the editor of a Labour paper.

So looking at him more closely, and marking particularly his mean and despicable features, I judged him to be a Member of the Chamber of Deputies, which corresponds with us to a Member of Parliament, and in this I was right.

MYSELF (*violently*) : " What will you do with this carrion ? "

FIRST MURDERER : " When we have rested a little we will take from him his fur coat and other things of value, which afterwards we will sell for money, and then we will let him go. For we have no rope with which to hang him, and to beat him about the head would be of no avail, seeing these men are not like others, but have beneath the bones of the skull a solid inductile substance impervious alike to arguments and blows."

MYSELF : " You speak very truly. For I have observed the same thing with our own Members of Parliament, who commonly consist of the refuse and scum of mankind. For they have no manners to speak of, but keep up a foolish bawling in that hall of theirs at Westminster which they call debate."

So the sun being now high in the heavens, and because I had determined to sleep that night at home, I buckled my stone jar beneath my coat and, after a very cordial farewell, went out from the grove of oak-trees and along the road that leads to the north.

Now the sun was by this time very hot, and I was presently minded to turn aside from the road towards a very good inn that I knew where I have often drunk ale, namely, the Inn of the Holy Trouts, which is within a league of Lautrec. And as I came by a bend in the road where there stands the little statue of St. Polycarp I saw a hale grey-haired man, very wide in the shoulders, sitting on a sack in the middle of the road. He had in his hand a kind of flail, very stout and strong, being formed of two ashen staves jointed with leather, for so the best flails were made before winnowing-machines were discovered and heresy and other abominations came into the land.

So I stood a while before the statue while I made my orisons, repeating the " Surge Domine " and the Athanasian Creed twice, with the Comminatory Clauses proper to the day.

And while I was praying the hale strong man arose, and with his flail beat violently upon the sack as it lay in the road, singing the while after this fashion :

> The Girls of Toulouse
> Wear stockings and shoes,
> Rubadub, rubadub, round about round.
> The men of Cahors
> Wear singlets and drawers
> (What I have lost will never be found),
> Rubadub, rubadub, round about round.

After he had paused a while to wipe his forehead,

for indeed it was a very violent exercise and he was
streaming with sweat, he commenced again, beating
and bawling like the devil when St. Bug caught
him in a basket :

> The People of Naas
> Go fasting to Mass,
> Roundabout, rubadub, all round about :
> But the people of Arques
> Cut their corns in the dark
> (A cup before sunrise is good for the gout),
> Roundabout, rubadub, roundabout out.

Now this singing of his and his manner of beating
the sack gave me a great feeling of satisfaction, for
I saw clearly that he was a very good and upright
man, so, having by this time finished my prayers,
I went up to him at once and said to him : " Will
you tell me what you have in the sack, and why
you beat it with your flail, and what is the name
of that fine song of yours ? For I know a great
many songs myself, but not that one." He replied
very courteously, but first, pulling the sack to the side
of the road, we sat upon it in order that we might
converse and have pleasure in each other's company.

THE STRANGER (*replying to my question*) : " As
to what I have in the sack, it is my wife, for you
must know that I am from St. Ives in Huntingdon-
shire, and I beat it and her inside it because it
is my humour and is good for the phlegm. As to
the name of the song, it is called Boula-biche, but
some call it ' The Lament of Marie-couche-toi-là.' "

MYSELF : " For my own part I like best those
songs that are made in Sussex, particularly the song
called ' Golier ', which I usually sing when I am

drinking ale ; but I know ninety-seven others, any one of which, or indeed all of them, I will sing to you if you wish it. For I see very clearly that we are of a mind in many important things."

THE STRANGER : "Do you know the song called 'Oyster Dumplings' ? "

MYSELF : "I have never heard it : was it made in Sussex ? "

THE STRANGER (*in a sudden bawling voice*) : "To the devil with all Sussex songs and the men who sing them ! For I am from St. Ives (as I have said), where we have very good songs of our own. And, further (to speak plainly), I would have you know that I and my wife are weary of your company."

Now this sudden fierce manner he had of speaking filled me with anger, and I rose from the sack where I had been sitting, though it had been in my mind to bear him company a little way on the road in order to discover (if it were possible) whether the men from St. Ives are web-fingered or no.

So I took the road alone, and after I had gone a little way the grey-haired man also rose to his feet and, first moistening the palms of his hands, fell again to his beating and singing, so that his voice came to me, strongly at first, but afterwards more faintly as I went along the road :

The Women of Nîmes
Are broad in the beam,
Rubadub, rubadub, round about round ;
But the men of St. Neots
Go to bed in their boots
(What I bought for a penny I sold for a pound),
Rubadub, rubadub, round about round.

But for my part I set my face to the sun and my back to the south wind, and, walking swiftly, came that evening to my home in the Good County (for so we call Sussex—or at least that part of it where I live, at Piddinghoe, below Arundel).

And when I had drunk some ale I went to bed.

But before I slept I composed a lament for the souls of those men who are not of Sussex, but live and die *in partibus infidelium*, particularly the men of Kent, who (as is commonly reported) fry pigs' feet with butter and have their wives in common.

So, commending myself to the saints and singing very joyfully, I fell asleep.

J. C. Squire

THE MERCIFUL WIDOW

(*John Masefield*)

INSIDE a cottage by a common
  There lived an aged widow woman.
She had twelve children (quite a lot),
And often wished that she had not.
" S'welp me," she often sighed, " I'd rather
You'd had a less prolific father ;
Better than raise this surging mob
That God had bowled me for a blob."

Amongst her seven strapping sons
There were some interesting ones.
Even the baby James, for instance,
Had killed a man without assistance ;

And several more in divers ways
Had striven to sing their Maker's praise.
Henry, quite small, had tried to smother
His somnolent recumbent mother;
Which failing, when she hollered fearful,
He looked upon her quite untearful,
With something of Don Juan's calm,
Proceeding thus without a qualm :—
" O mother in our hours of ease,
As irritating as ten fleas,
When pain and anguish wring the brow
A fatuously lethargic sow,
This time I haven't put you through it,
But if you wait a day or two, it
Will be quite clear I mean to do it."
Whereat the mother murmured " Law !
I'll gi'e yer a wipe acrost the jaw ! "
Another son, Ezekiel,
Was well upon the road to hell,
Once every fortnight he betrayed
An unsuspecting village maid,
And now and then he went much furder
By rounding off the job with murder.
Sometimes they took him to the 'sizes,
But there he told outrageous lieses,
His loving family, unblushing,
Always unanimously rushing
To help him with false alibises.
Richard was just another such,
But William, Sam and John were much
More evil and debauched than these.
The account of their atrocities
Might make a smelting furnace freeze.
Without a scintilla of shame

They bragged of things I cannot name.
I represent them here by blanks.

— — — — — — — — — —

(READER : " For this relief much thanks ! ")

Hedda Lucrezia Esther Waters,
The eldest of the widow's daughters,
In early infancy absorbéd
A dreadful liking for the morbid.
She much preferred the works of Ibsen
To those of Mr. Dana Gibson,
And when she went to bed at night
She prayed by yellow candle-light :
" Six angels for my bed,
Three at foot and three at head,
Beardsley, Strauss, Augustus John,
Bless the bed that I lie on.
Nietzsche, Maeterlinck, Matisse,
Fold my sleep in holy peace."
The vices to which she inclined
Were peccadilloes of the mind.
Her sisters were much less refined,
And often when they sallied out,
With knife and pistol, kris and knout
And other weapons of the sort
Adapted to bucolic sport
And rural raptures in the dark,
They took occasion to remark :
" Why, wot the 'ell's the —— use
O 'Edda, she ain't got no juice,
She'll gas and jabber till all's blue ;
She'll talk but she will never do.
Upon my oath, it is fair sickenin'."

And so at last they gave her strychnine,
A thing efficient though not gory.
And Hedda drops from out the story.

Four daughters, seven sons were left,
But still the widow felt bereft,
She was distressed at Hedda's loss,
And found it hard to bear her cross.
She tried to find a salve for it
By studying in Holy Writ.
She read the exciting episode
Of how good Moses made a road
Across the rubicundish ocean,
But could not stifle her emotion.
She read of Jews and Jebusites,
And Hittites and Amalekites,
And Joash, Job and Jeroboam,
And Rachel, Ruth and Rehoboam,
And Moloch, Moab and Megiddo,
But still no respite had the widow.
Nothing could charm her grief away,
It grew more bitter every day.
Often she'd sit when evening fell,
And moan : " Ah, Lawkamussy, well,
'Edda was better than the rest,
My 'Edda allus was the best.
Many's the time she's washed the crocks,
And scrubbed the floors and darned the socks.
When all them selfish gals an' blokes
Was out, the selfish things they are,
A-murderin' and a-rapin' folks,
'Edda would stay 'ome with 'er ma.
Yes, 'Edda was a lovely chile,
I do remember 'er sweet smile,

'Er little 'ands wot lammed and lugged me,
An' scratched an' tore an' pinched an' tugged me.
I mind me 'ow so long ago,
I set 'er little cheeks aglow,
When I 'ad bin to Ledbury fair
An' bought a ribbon for 'er 'air,
A ribbon for 'er pretty 'ead ;
But now my little 'Edda's dead !
Now while spring pulses through the blood
And jonquils carpet every wood,
And God's small fowls sing in the dawn,
I wish to Gawd I'd naver bin born ! "

And so at last the widow thought
Things were not going as they ought.
She'd never grumbled in the past :
She'd let them all do things at which
Most parents would have stood aghast—
She'd seen it all without a twitch.
Indeed, religiously she'd tried
To share the joy and fun they'd had ;
But really this sororicide
Was coming it a bit too bad.
She made her mind up : " It's high time
They stopped their silly vice and crime ! "
She mustered the domestic throng
And gave it to them hot and strong.
" Look here," she said, " this —— flux
'Ad best come to a —— crux !
I long regarded as diversions
Your profligacies and perversions ;
I helped you while you swam in sin,
And backed you up through thick and thin ;

But now you've gone a step too far;
I mean to show you I'm your ma.
Yes, it's you I'm talkin' to, Kate and John :
You'll have to stop these goings-on.
Murders must stop from this day on ! "

Sons and daughters stood amazed,
Bunkered, flummuxed, moonstruck, dazed,
Grunted with appropriate swear,
" What's come over the old mare ?
Stop the murders, stop the drink,
Stop the lechery ? I don't fink ! "
" If she's had enough of sin,
I guess we'd better do 'er in ! "
Thus said Henry, savagely
Whetting his knife upon his knee.
" No," said James, " go easy, brother ;
After all, she is our mother.
Just you wait for 'arf a mo' —
Give me 'arf a mo' to show
'Er the thing in a new light,
And mother'll come round all right ! "

Love is and was our king and lord,
The tongue is mightier than the sword,
Words may shine at break of day
Like a palace of Cathay,
Words may shine when evening falls
Like the sign of three brass balls.
All the crowd cried, " Righto, Jim !
Jim's a plucked 'un, 'ark to 'im ! "
Chewing half-a-pound of twist,
Smiting the table with his fist,

Jim went on : " Just 'ark to me,
Mother, jest you 'ark to me."
(He spat with vigour on his hands)
" This is 'ow the matter stands.

" I'll agree we've done enough
Stabbin's, drunks and such-like stuff,
We, unlike our fellow-men,
Have fractured the commandments ten
With others of our own invention
That the scripture doesn't mention.
We have done to heart's content.

— — — — — — — — — —
— — — — — — — — — —

And speaking for myself, I've had
Quite enough of being bad ;
And to cut the matter short,
Should find uprightness quite good sport.
But, mother, mother, strike me blind,
This must aye be borne in mind,
Mother, mother, strike me rotten,
This must never be forgotten,
We must not think of self alone.
If no one's interests but our own
Were here involved we'd all turn pi,
And put our past transgressions by.
We'd gladly cease our evil-doings,
Promiscuous assaults and wooings,
And end the too-familiar scenes
Which you indignantly have eyed ;
Only, alas, our hands are tied,
Another factor intervenes.
For there's a poet up in London
Who, if we stop, will be quite undone,

We do evil for his good,
He inks his paper with our blood ;
Every crime that we commit
He makes a poem out of it,
And were we so unkind's to stop, he
Would famish for congenial copy.
My life begins to give my guts hell,
But there's the matter in a nutshell."

"Ay, ay," said Dick, in accents cold,
"Brother Jim the truth has told."
"Ay, ay," the girls said, "do not doubt it,
That's the truth, that's all about it."
"Well," said the mother, "I am human,
Though only a poor widow woman.
Jim's remarks have cleared my sight,
I understand your motives quite,
And when you shed pore 'Edda's blood
Your purpose was distinctly good.
I still must make it understood
I do not like your goings-on,
Espeshly yours, Bill, Sam and John.
But contraventions of the laws
Committed in such worthy cause,
Habits, however atavistic,
Prompted by feelings altruistic,
I can't view with disapprobation
Entirely without qualification.
Thought of your evil deeds must pain me,
Thoughts of your motives must restrain me,
I'm proud to find such virtue in you;
As far as I'm concerned, continue."

NUMEROUS CELTS

THERE'S a grey wind wails on the clover,
  And grey hills, and mist around the hills,
And a far voice sighing a song that is over,
  And my grey heart that a strange longing fills.

A sheen of dead swords that shake upon the wind,
  And a harp that sleeps though the wind is blowing
Over the hills and the seas and the great hills
    behind,
  The great hills of Kerry, where my heart would
    be going.

For I would be in Kerry now where quiet is the
    grass,
  And the birds are crying in the low light,
And over the stone hedges the shadows pass,
  And a fiddle weeps at the shadow of the night.

              With Pat Doogan
              Father Murphy
              Brown maidens
              King Cuchullain
              The Kine
              The Sheep
              Some old women
              Some old men
  And Uncle White Sea-gull and all.

(*Chorus*) And Uncle White Sea-gull and all.

(H. G. Wells)

I

I DO not quite know how to begin. . . . Ever since I left England and settled here in this quiet Putumayo valley I have been wondering and wondering. . . . I want to put everything down quite frankly so that you who come after me shall understand. It is very peaceful here in the forest, and as my mind goes back to that roaring old England, with its strange welter of aspirations and basenesses, that little old England, so far away now, a small green jewel in the great sea, I break into a smile of tender tolerance. Here, as the immemorial procession of day and night, of summer and winter, sweeps over the earth, amid the vast serenities of primeval nature, it all seems so very far away, so small, so queerly inconsequent. . . . The men who made me, the men who broke me, the women I loved, the sprawling towns, the confused effort, and that ungainly lop-sided structure of our twentieth-century civilization, with its strange welter of sex. . . .

II

And then it was that the Hon. Astarte Cholmondeley came into my life. I remember as clearly as though it were yesterday—and it is now over thirty years ago—the moment of our meeting. It was at one of those enormous futile receptions that political hostesses give at the beginning of the Session, assemblies of two or three thousand men and women, minor politicians, organizers, journalists, all clamorous for champagne and burning for nods of recognition from the great men of the Party. It was a fine night, almost oppressively warm, and I had walked across the Park from Hill Street, carrying my opera-hat in my hand. There was a dull uniform roar from the distant traffic ; the tops of the trees faintly swished in the light wind, the lights along the lake shone very quietly, and above were the vast serenities of the sky, powdered with stars. On benches in the shadows lurked pairs of quiet lovers, and the stars looked down upon them as they had upon lovers in Nineveh and Babylon. As I stepped out into the rush of Pall Mall, with its stream of swift motors, I thought, I remember, of my career. . . .

III

The crush was vulgar and intolerable.

I had spent an hour passing dejected remarks to the other young men, also there out of duty and as bored as I was myself. Then suddenly she entered . . . a slender slip of a thing—brown-haired and brown-eyed, leaning flower-like on the arm of her elephantine mother, the Dowager. . . .

IV

" Dearest," she wrote me next day, " did you sleep last night ? I did not sleep a wink. All night long I lay dazzled and overwhelmed by this wonderful thing that has come to us. And then this morning, when God's great dawn slowly lifted over the westward hills, I got up, did my hair (oh my beautiful, beautiful hair, now all yours, my own Man, all yours), and sat down to write this, my first letter, to you. I am sitting at the little win-

dow of my room in the Lion Tower. The breath
of the roses rises in the fresh morning air; and
out beyond the park, where the deer are placidly
grazing, the slanting sun glints exquisitely on
spacious woodland and rolling down, mile after
mile. . . . Far away, against the blue of the
horizon, there is a little pointing church spire, and
somehow it reminds me of you. . . . Oh, my lover,
I am going to lay bare to you the inmost shrine
of my heart. You must be patient with me, very
patient; for do we not belong to each other?
We must live openly we two, we who are the
apostles of new freedoms, of new realizations, of
a second birth for this dear, foolish old world of
ours." Thus she wrote, and there was more, much
more, too sacredly intimate to be set down here,
but breathing in every line the essence of her ador-
able self. . . .

v

And then it was that Mary Browne came into
my life. I had known her years ago when I was
at college; I had thought her a meek and rather
dull little girl, as insignificant as the rest of her
family. But now there was about her a certain
quality of graciousness, very difficult to define,
but very unescapable when it is present, that gave
to her mouse-grey hair and rather weak blue eyes
a beauty very rare and very subtle. She had spent,
she told me, two years in the East End at some
social work or other. . . .

vi

And then I met Cecilia Scroop. . . .

VII

And so the end came. In those last days I worked more feverishly than ever, writing my book, attending committees, speaking on platforms throughout the country. I was the chief speaker during that by-election of Brooks's at Manchester, which I still believe might have been the germ of a new social order, of coherences and approximations, of differentiations and realizations beyond the imagining of the men of our time, but to be very clearly and very palpably apprehended by that future race for whom we, in a blind and groping way, are living and building. . . . And then the blow fell. . . .

It was a Friday afternoon. The House had risen early after throwing out some absurd Bill that that ass Biffin had brought in ; I think it was something about Bee Disease. I had been one of the tellers for the Noes, and at three o'clock I walked out into Palace Yard and along the chalky stone cloister that leads to the private tunnel through which members enter the Underground Railway station. I had promised to meet Astarte at four at the foot of the Scenic Railway (this was before the time when little Higgins revolutionized the amusement business with his actino-gyroscopes) in the Earl's Court Exhibition. Since her marriage with Binger communication had been increasingly difficult for us. All her letters were opened, and Binger had eavesdroppers at work in the telephone exchanges. Her chauffeur, happily, played his master false, and she was usually able to keep appointments when she had made them ; and for

some months we had arranged our meetings by little
cryptic notices in the agony column of the *Morning
Post*. We had thought ourselves safe. But she
must have dropped a casual word to somebody ;
some fool had given us away ; and when I got to
Earl's Court I found that Astarte was there, but
that Mary and Cecilia were there as well. . . .

VIII

I remonstrated with them. I knew it was hopeless, and my heart sank ; but I did my best. Greatest agony of all it was to know that these women
in whom I had trusted, whom I had looked to
as pioneers, as auguries of what was to be and what
still will be, were, when the crisis came, still shackled
and bound by the little petty jealousies of the old
system. With set, white faces they glowered
upon me (it was raining a little, I remember, and
the ground at our feet was muddy and covered
with stained and trampled paper) as I spoke, softly
and passionately, of muddle and waste, of the
sordid and furtive shames and reticences that man
has brought with him from the ancestral past,
that he must shed before we build for our gods
the diviner temples that might be. . . . Night
came over . . . and then, as my voice failed, a
tall man stepped out from behind a hoarding.
It was Montacute, the Prime Minister. " I am
very sorry for you," he said simply, " but I am
afraid, Mr. Bilgewater, we shall have to ask you
to resign." He seemed to hesitate a moment ;
then, as though half ashamed, he held out his hand
and looked me in the eyes . . . I had known him

since I was a boy at school and he a young man,
a fastidious and kindly young man who had seemed
almost too delicate for the rough work of politics.
He had always taken a friendly interest in me
even when I was bitterly fighting him . . . " Good-
bye," he said. My voice was husky as I returned
his farewell.

IX

I went back to my chambers and told my man
to pack a single portmanteau. There were just
three hours before the boat-train. Before I left
I wrote ten letters. . . .

IF POPE HAD WRITTEN " BREAK, BREAK, BREAK "

(Pope)

FLY, Muse, thy wonted themes, nor longer
    seek
The consolations of a powder'd cheek ;
Forsake the busy purlieus of the Court
For calmer meads where finny tribes resort.
So may th' Almighty's natural antidote
Abate the worldly tenour of thy note,
The various beauties of the liquid main
Refine thy reed and elevate thy strain.

See how the labour of the urgent oar
Propels the barks and draws them to the shore.
Hark ! from the margin of the azure bay
The joyful cries of infants at their play.

(The offspring of a piscatorial swain,
His home the sands, his pasturage the main.)
Yet none of these may soothe the mourning heart,
Nor fond alleviation's sweets impart ;
Nor may the pow'rs of infants that rejoice
Restore the accents of a former voice,
Nor the bright smiles of ocean's nymphs command
The pleasing contact of a vanished hand.
So let me still in meditation move,
Muse in the vale and ponder in the grove,
And scan the skies where sinking Phœbus glows
With hues more rubicund than Cibber's nose. . . .
(*After which the poet gets into his proper stride.*)

G. K. Chesterton

VARIATIONS ON AN AIR

*Composed on Having to Appear in a Pageant as
Old King Cole*

OLD King Cole was a merry old soul,
  And a merry old soul was he ;
   He called for his pipe,
   He called for his bowl,
  And he called for his fiddlers three.

After Lord Tennyson.

Cole, that unwearied prince of Colchester,
Growing more gay with age and with long days
Deeper in laughter and desire of life,
As that Virginian climber on our walls
Flames scarlet with the fading of the year ;
Called for his wassail and that other weed

Virginian also, from the western woods
Where English Raleigh checked the boast of Spain;
And lighting joy with joy, and piling up
Pleasure as crown for pleasure, bade men bring
Those three, the minstrels whose emblazoned coats
Shone with the oyster-shells of Colchester;
And these three played, and playing grew more fain
Of mirth and music; till the heathen came,
And the King slept beside the northern sea.

After W. B. Yeats.

Of an old King in a story
  From the grey sea-folk I have heard,
Whose heart was no more broken
  Than the wings of a bird.

As soon as the moon was silver
  And the thin stars began,
He took his pipe and his tankard,
  Like an old peasant man.

And three tall shadows were with him
  And came at his command;
And played before him for ever
  The fiddles of fairyland.

And he died in the young summer
  Of the world's desire;
Before our hearts were broken
  Like sticks in a fire.

After Robert Browning.

Who smoke-snorts toasts o' My Lady Nicotine,
Kicks stuffing out of Pussyfoot, bids his trio

Stick up their Stradivarii (that's the plural)
Or near enough, my fatheads ; *nimium*
Vicina Cremonœ ; that's a bit too near.)
Is there some stockfish fails to understand ?
Catch hold o' the notion, bellow and blurt back
    " Cole " ?
Must I bawl lessons from a horn-book, howl,
Cat-call the cat-gut " fiddles " ? Fiddlesticks !

After Walt Whitman.

Me clairvoyant,
Me conscious of you, old camarado,
Needing no telescope, lorgnette, field-glass, opera-
    glass, myopic pince-nez,
Me piercing two thousand years with eye naked
    and not ashamed ;
The crown cannot hide you from me ;
Musty old feudal-heraldic trappings cannot hide
    you from me,
I perceive that you drink.
(I am drinking with you. I am as drunk as you
    are.)
I see you are inhaling tobacco, puffing, smoking,
    spitting
(I do not object to your spitting),
You prophetic of American largeness,
You anticipating the broad masculine manners of
    these States ;
I see in you also there are movements, tremors,
    tears, desire for the melodious,
I salute your three violinists, endlessly making
    vibrations,
Rigid, relentless, capable of going on for ever ;

They play my accompaniment; but I shall take
    no notice of any accompaniment;
I myself am a complete orchestra.
So long.

After Swinburne.

In the time of old sin without sadness
    And golden with wastage of gold,
Like the gods that grow old in their gladness
    Was the king that was glad, growing old:
And with sound of loud lyres from his palace
    The voice of his oracles spoke,
And the lips that were red from his chalice
    Were splendid with smoke.

When the weed was as flame for a token
    And the wine was as blood for a sign;
And upheld in his hands and unbroken
    The fountains of fire and of wine.
And a song without speech, without singer,
    Stung the soul of a thousand in three,
As the flesh of the earth has to sting her,
    The soul of the sea.

Susan Miles

HE SPORTS BY HIMSELF
(*Thomas Hardy*)

ON Christmas morn awake did I,
    And stare at the murkèd sodden sky,
    The sodden sky.

I said : " On Poldon Top the rime
Makes silvern fretwork. 'Tis no crime
To seek the haunts of former time.
  All here's awry."

Past Yellham Hill I vamped my way,
And as I stalked I bore a tray,
  A dinted tray,
My arm beneath, of metal made,
Britannia called. For naught I stayed,
Though dull brats gaped and sheep-dogs bayed
  And an ass did bray.

I sweated much on Poldon Top ;
I loosed the scarf which I had wrop,
  Grimly had wrop
My neck around. Not as whilom,
Though doggedly, the hill I'd clomb.
My boot heels, clogged with frozen loam,
  Made dismal plop.

Scowling, upon my tray I perched ;
To right and left I swung and lurched,
  Wanzing I lurched.
The frore wind caused my nose to drip ;
A ruthless bough bruised chest and hip ;
My stomach heaved as on a ship ;
  My heart I searched.

I said : " Not now as days of yore,
As merry days of heretofore,
  Long heretofore ;

For once ten yelling blithe-eyed wights,
With muscles taut and joyous sprites,
Tobogganed here, and sailed their kites ;
    Nine nevermore.''

The moon was up as home I tramped,
Not as at day-break I had vamped,
    Had sturdily vamped ;
For my agèd bones were aching sore ;
My tree-scratched face was caked with gore ;
Night mists had chilled me to the core ;
    My sprite was damped.

Each of that laughing circle, save
One, now lies mouldering in his grave,
    Worm-riddled grave.
I only live to bear my tray
To Poldon Top this Christmas day,
And with nine phasms zestless play
    That grin and rave.

Colin D. B. Ellis

THE NEW VICAR OF BRAY,
OR, TIME-SERVING UP-TO-DATE

IN Queen Victoria's early days,
    When Grandpapa was Vicar,
The squire was worldly in his ways,
    And far too fond of liquor.
My grandsire laboured to exhort
    This influential sinner,
As to and fro they passed the port
    On Sunday after dinner.

My father stepped Salvation's road
  To tunes of Tate and Brady's ;
His congregation overflowed
  With wealthy maiden ladies.
Yet modern thought he did not shirk—
  He made his contribution
By writing that successful work,
  " The Church and Evolution."

When I took orders, war and strife
  Filled parsons with misgiving,
For none knew who might lose his life
  Or who might lose his living.
But I was early on the scenes,
  Where some were loth to go, sir !
And there by running Base Canteens
  I won the D.S.O., sir !

You may have read " The Verey Light "—
  A book of verse that I penned—
The proceeds of it, though but slight,
  Eked out my modest stipend.
My grandsire's tactics long had failed,
  And now my father's line did ;
So on another tack I sailed
  (You can't be too broad-minded).

The public-house is now the place
  To get to know the men in,
And if the King is in disgrace
  Then I shall shout for Lenin !

And though my feelings they may shock,
  By murder, theft and arson,
The parson still shall keep his flock
  While they will keep the parson!

And this is the law that I'll maintain
  Until my dying day, sir!
That whether King or Mob shall reign,
  I'm for the people that pay, sir!

INDEX

The Fireside Library

General Editor:
ARTHUR COMPTON RICKETT, M.A., LL.D.

FIVE SHILLINGS NET

Songs from the Elizabethans

Chosen by **J. C. Squire**

With an Introductory Essay

A charming collection of poetic songs written in the days when "Good Queen Bess" was a power in the land, and although many of them will be familiar to students and lovers of old English folk-songs, there are a number of other gems which will make a strong appeal to those who delight in the ballads written in those far-off days.

The
Fireside Library

General Editor :

ARTHUR COMPTON RICKETT, M.A., LL.D.

FIVE SHILLINGS NET

The
Old-World Pleasaunce

by **ELEANOUR SINCLAIR ROHDE,**

Author of " A Garden of Herbs," " The Old English Herbals," " The Old English Gardening Books," etc.

An anthology compiled from mediæval, Elizabethan and Stuart gardening writers and treating of : (I) Mediæval Gardens. (*a*) The Garden in Spring, (*b*) A Monastery Garden, (*c*) Royal Gardens, (*d*) Castle Gardens, (*e*) A Mystic Garden ; (II) Elizabethan and Stuart Gardens, The Joys of Gardening and the Pleasures of a Garden, The Gardener, Women Gardeners, "Lovesome Flowers," Sundial Mottoes of the Sixteenth and Seventeenth Centuries, The Orchard, The Garden of Eden, Bee Lore.

The Times — " Full of ingratiating oddities and of real charm."